The Will

The Will to Live

A HOLISTIC APPROACH TO LIFE-THREATENING DISEASES

PETREA KING

THORSONS PUBLISHING GROUP

First UK edition published 1990

Originally published in 1988 by Equinox Publishing, a division of the Craftsman's Press, Pty. Limited, Upper Level, 108 Pacific Highway, Roseville, NSW 2069, Australia

British Library Cataloguing in Publication Data

King, Petrea
The will to live: a holistic approach to
life-threatening diseases.
1. Man. diseases. Psychological aspects
I. Title
616.0019

ISBN 0-7225-2215-0

Published by Thorsons Publishers Limited,
Wellingborough, Northamptonshire, NN8 2RQ, England.

Printed in Great Britain by Hartnolls Limited, Bodmin, Cornwall

1 3 5 7 9 10 8 6 4 2

Dedication

To my mother, Rae,
When I was a little girl, the only way I could tidy my bedroom was if my mother sat on the end of my bed, offering me encouragement and the occasional directive.

This book came into being in much the same way. Without her constant presence and encouragement, these words would never have been committed to paper,

and,

to my godson, Morgan Anthony Potter, born 27 February 1988, whose entrance into the world symbolises the spirit behind this book.

Acknowledgements

If I were to acknowledge all the people who have helped directly or indirectly to bring this book into being, it would form a book of its own.

My gratitude goes to all the people I have had the privilege of working with over the years. And to my children, Kate and Simon, who entertained themselves whilst their mum pounded away on typewriter keys.

"This is a powerful book for people who are willing to take responsibility for their lives, and who are willing to change their lives by changing the thoughts in their minds."

GERALD JAMPOLSKY MD
Founder and Consultant
Center for Attitudinal Healing
Tiburon, California.

The most minute transformation
is like a pebble
dropped into a still lake.
The ripples spread out endlessly.

CONTENTS

Introduction

One day a friend and I visited a waterfall deep within a National Park. It was a soft and drizzly day. The heavier rains of the previous days had left the air crisp and clear. Diamond raindrops hung from the leaves everywhere and the river roared as it rushed its way to the cliff's edge. There were two lookouts; one immediately above the waterfall and another some 300 metres distant, down a slippery path scattered with puddles and tree roots. The first lookout afforded us a wonderful view of the volume of water and the canopy of rainforest deep below, into which this river tumbled. We decided to walk around to the second lookout.

On our way, we met a lady who was returning from viewing the falls from this second lookout. We greeted her. She barely looked up but was quick to tell us it was not worth our while to go any further, as the view was much better from the first lookout. We thanked her but continued on our way. On our arrival at the viewing place our breath was taken away by the beauty spread before us. Though it was still drizzling lightly, the sun had broken through, and not only had it lent a wonderful golden glow to the scene before us, but it had created a beautiful double rainbow right across the waterfall.

After some minutes we began our return trip and on our way met another couple who, becoming discouraged by the path, enquired whether it was worth their while to continue. We assured them there was a wonderful view awaiting them and they continued on with lighter step and more enthusiasm.

I realised at that moment how much my philosophy is reflected in my work. We cannot always change the outcome of any situation but we can certainly always change the way in which we experience that outcome. It is not the destination or goal which should preoccupy us, but how we take every step along the way to achieving that goal. Life is made up of many steps in a desired direction. Those steps can be made with heavy and fearful heart or they can be made lightly, with joy in each step. As the old Chinese proverb says, 'It is better to travel than to arrive.' Some people are so pre-occupied with the view — the end-result — that the beauty and knowledge gained on the journey itself are lost.

In September 1983, I was diagnosed with acute leukaemia. I was told it was a very unusual aggressive type and I 'wouldn't see Christmas', which was only a matter of weeks away. The sense of complete shock and apprehension will be known to many of my readers. The mind becomes immobilised and we experience a sense of unreality which negates our ability to think clearly. It races through a myriad of emotions and reactions. One moment there is denial, ('He can't be right; I don't feel *that* sick'). To anger, ('Why me' or 'Why now?'). To anguish, ('How will I tell my family?'), and so on.

This initial response to such a diagnosis is entirely natural and to be expected. The diagnosis of being HIV-positive* may well be compounded by the fact that the person may not wish their health status to be known to anyone. It can be tremendously isolating and frightening. The stress of such a 'secret' alone, can be detrimental to one's health.

It is only in recent years we can talk openly about cancer. Previously it was considered unmentionable because it was synonymous with suffering and death, and there was a certain mystique surrounding the disease to which only doctors were privy. Fortunately this has changed dramatically. Now there is much enlightened literature freely available in the community about cancer and its treatments.

The stigma attached to being HIV positive is still prevalent and the sooner we, as a community, can put it aside, the sooner real solutions to the problems it raises can be addressed. In our society we are geared to believe that what we are told is true, whether the information comes to us through the media, through our educational system or across a doctor's desk. Until

* *HIV stands for 'Human Immunodeficiency Virus'. These initials will be used throughout the book to denote infection with the virus. Where the initials AIDS are used, it denotes the condition of full AIDS. Being infected with the HIV is in no way an automatic diagnosis of AIDS.*

recently we never considered questioning our physician's diagnosis, advice or treatments. However, over recent years people have become much more informed about their own bodies, their general health and their fitness. This education on the part of the public has led to the individual's desire, when sick, to understand both the disease and the prescribed treatments. People are also wanting to be involved in their own healing process and to assist in whatever way they can to restore themselves to full health.

As we discover more about the human body and what it requires to remain healthy, it gives us clues to the avenues worthy of exploration when it is diseased. We are beginning to understand health is not just being free of disease. We are hearing more about 'peak fitness', 'optimum health'. Everywhere there are Government-backed projects educating the public in better health. No diseases strike more fear into our hearts than cancer and AIDS. The fact that so many in our community consider these to be synonymous with death, or long, painful, degrading treatments, does not help us at a time when we need tremendous emotional support. To use the word 'terminal' about a patient is to overlook the exceptional, the miraculous.

The word 'terminal' should only ever be used in connection with trains, buses and aeroplanes and should never be used about people. So many people have survived these 'terminal' diseases. All people should be given the opportunity to be the exception. This book is written for those who are living with a life-threatening disease, not dying from a terminal one. There are no dying people. Either we are alive, or we are dead.

An essential quality for happiness is the feeling of being in control. To be without hope, without choice or without influence over our life, is the antithesis of being at peace.

In the following pages we will explore many ways in which we can take, and maintain, control over our lives. Some of these skills and techniques I discovered through my own experience of healing. Since my recovery, many more have been added through my work with thousands of people. I have been enriched and educated by each individual who has shared with me their joys, sorrows, problems and solutions. It is the synthesis of these experiences which form the basis of this book.

When people are taking an active part in their healing process, they have a sense of hope and control. It helps establish peace of mind as we create an environment for healing. The journey, like that to the waterfall lookout, assumes a richness and dimension otherwise overlooked. We may not be able to change the outcome of our disease, but we certainly can change the way in which we experience that outcome. With peace of mind and a positive outlook, any healing that can take place, certainly will do so. Miracles do happen, and often! Our medical community classifies these miracles as 'spontaneous remissions'. These 'spontaneous remissions' mainly seem to come about in people who have put a great deal of effort into their recovery, and who have an underlying belief and faith in their ability to affect the outcome of their disease process.

The thoughts and attitudes which we hold can advance the healing process within our bodies. It defies common sense to think of a content and well-functioning immune system, heart or liver in the body of someone who is continually angry or upset with his or her world. Likewise, if a person is chronically depressed or pessimistic. Our mind is not separate from our body. Our emotions are not separate from our body. As human beings we are an integrated whole. The thoughts we hold in our minds must affect our total functioning. The feelings we have, whether acknowledged or ignored, must have an effect on our whole being.

Our mind has the extraordinary capacity to change thoughts it holds dear. This gives us a tremendous point of power. We can change thoughts which cause us stress into those which lay foundations for greater peace, fulfilment and joy in our lives. In this way we can enhance our healing process. This choice is unique to humankind.

Each person must find their own path to healing. It is a path of self-understanding and acknowledgement; the path you choose will be uniquely your own. We will explore the possibilities of healing on all levels, and investigate the process of letting go and trusting the spirit within.

Chapter One

Creating the Environment for Healing

It may be an extraordinary statement to many people, but I am no longer surprised when someone in our support group says they are 'grateful' for the experience of cancer or AIDS. I say 'grateful' in inverted commas because most will qualify the statement by saying they would prefer not to have the disease, but are grateful for what they have learned about themselves, and life in general, by having it. In many ways I feel my life began once I was diagnosed with leukaemia. A diagnosis of a life-threatening disease can be a tremendous opportunity for personal growth and understanding. It certainly takes a conscious choice on the part of the individual to see it that way! We can feel like the victim of a disease or we can choose, as far as possible, to take responsibility for our situation: to remain in control. After the shock of the initial diagnosis has worn off, we can look at what it means to us to be in this situation and what we may be able to do to assist ourselves in our healing. It can be a useful exercise at this point, or at any other point during our healing process, to write down answers to the following questions:

Do I really want to be well again?
Why do I want to live?
Am I willing to take responsibility for my health/life?
In what areas of my life am I not fully living?

These may seem surprising questions to ask. We think, of course, we want to live. It is not always so though. Many people calmly accept their diagnosis and the outcome of their disease. Many will happily hand over the responsibility for their health to their doctor, and will play no active role in getting well. These people need to either change their attitude to life, or concentrate on improving the quality of their remaining time.

Society generally accepts that 'living' is a positive thing, and to think or talk about 'dying' is a negative pastime. This has changed considerably through the work of Elisabeth Kübler-

Ross and others in recent years. However, it is still commonly felt among doctors that treatment has been 'successful' when they have 'saved' someone's life, and they have 'failed' when the patient dies. This criterion is a really inappropriate one. If we are to use the qualification of success or failure, then success surely must be people living with a good quality of life, with joy and fulfilment in every day lived, until they die with peace and dignity. Failure can only be living or dying in fear or in emotional isolation. If you decide, 'I have been successful only if I overcome this disease', you are also affirming, 'I have failed if I die.'

If we make peace of mind our one goal, we are also creating the perfect environment for healing within our body. To achieve peace of mind is a challenge at any time. To achieve it whilst living with a life-threatening disease is a victory indeed! Many people have done so by employing the techniques outlined within this book. We can choose to experience this illness as an adventure in exploring our inner nature, to find our abilities, talents, feelings, unfulfilled dreams and aspirations. We can learn to appreciate life more fully by really enjoying every day lived, not worrying or being pre-occupied with the future or the past but savouring each moment as it unfolds.

Choosing our Physician

One of the major factors in our process of healing is our relationship with our physician. We need a good working relationship with our doctor in which we feel free to communicate and ask questions. We, as patients, are not looking for statistics. We are looking for positive healing through the establishment of hope and a loving, supportive environment combined with expert medical treatment. Only harm can come from pronouncements like, 'I don't expect you to see Christmas' (a very popular one!), or, wittily expressed by another, 'I wouldn't take out Life Insurance if I were you', or some other reference to a time limit. Unexpected healings take place frequently. These are called 'spontaneous remissions' by the medical profession. If we call a disease 'terminal' we eliminate the possibility of the exceptional, whereas to call a disease 'life-threatening' gives a sense of possibility.

My belief is that no life can be truly threatened because we are eternal, and our life is not determined by being in a body. I believe if I go out of remission and die, it is simply because I have completed whatever it was I came here to do. My expectation, however, is that I shall remain in remission for another 50 or 60 years!

So, back to our choice of doctor. There is no harm in changing your doctor if you do not feel comfortable with the one you have. You may feel fear at the thought of leaving a certain physician because he has been pronounced 'the best'. Ask yourself: the 'best' at what? If he will help you to die according to his timetable then a change of doctor is certainly in order. Choose a doctor who will help you to live up to your full potential with your own brand of courage and perception. More and more doctors are understanding the need for this, so make it your priority to find one. If it is not possible for you to find a doctor who meets these requirements, then decide you will employ his expertise and you will seek your emotional support elsewhere.

Many hospitals now have support groups for people with life-threatening diseases and these can be very valuable. There is a chapter in this book devoted to support groups and how they function. If there is not a support group in your area, this chapter provides the information on how one can be set up.

There is nothing in this book which in any way contra-indicates traditional medical care. What I believe should happen when you go to your doctor and are diagnosed with cancer or AIDS is that he should explain, 'Yes, you do have a life-threatening disease and this is how I would like to treat it ...', and then go on to say, 'What I would like you to do though, is really look to your nutrition, make sure you are having a really first-class diet. Perhaps get some advice on the vitamins or minerals which may help you through this time. Look at the stresses you have in your life and how you are dealing with them. Perhaps learn some techniques of relaxation, visualisation and meditation, so you can establish a centre of calm within yourself and develop the power behind the positive attitude which you want to nuture. Find suitable exercise within your present capabilities. Read inspiring books about courageous people who have overcome obstacles in their life. In this way you can contribute a great deal to your healing process.'

Thus, knowing what *he* can do for you medically, and armed with the knowledge of all the things which *you* can do to help yourself, by the time you leave your doctor, you feel really positive about your future.

Our Home Environment

A supportive home environment is essential to our spirits. To be surrounded by co-operative and positive people who have an underlying belief in our ability to overcome whatever obstacles are in our way, is more than half the battle. These obstacles may include our fears and anxieties about our health, our treatment, our uncertainties of the future, our frustrations, or the more immediate issues of our pain, nausea or confusion. A discussion with your family of your needs in this area can prove to be very valuable in assisting you to create the ideal environment for your healing. It is often difficult for us to articulate our needs as, perhaps, it is something which we are unaccustomed to doing. However, that is no reason to postpone the discussion.

One mother, Jane, said in one of the support groups that she didn't want to tell her children the cancer had returned because she thought it would upset them. She thought she could hold out as long as possible and then, when the time was right, she would simply disappear into the bushland surrounding their home. In some obscure way she believed the children wouldn't really notice her absence, and they would continue their lives undisturbed. These children were 18, 19 and 25 years of age and had done very little physically to support their mother as she had been determined to keep up her role as homemaker. After discussing her thoughts with and getting feedback from the support group, she decided to share with her children and her church (which played a large part in her life) the fact she had secondaries from her original cancer. She was flooded with support and caring. Her family freely expressed their feelings and could stop the pretence of 'everything is fine'. Often when we try to protect others from emotional upset, we compound the problem. The fact is, this family was living with unacknowledged and unexpressed sadness anyway. Through Jane's courage in talking about it with them, it gave the 'O.K.' to expressing those pent-up emotions. It also allowed the family to express support in a positive, practical and meaningful way. A Mass was held in her home shortly before her death and the home was full of loving and supportive people. Dozens of people attended this Mass and Jane was deeply touched, not realising just how much she was loved and appreciated by those in her life. She attended the support group right up until the week before her death and her peace and radiance was clearly visible.

There are some people in the world whose lives are full of woe and misery. They delight in commiserating with us about our 'bad luck' in receiving such an 'unfortunate' diagnosis. They seem to thrive on the negative and abhor the positive. Avoid these people if at all possible, or, if you live with one, discuss the effect this thinking has on you. This attitude is anything but empathetic. It pulls down our spirits very quickly. Empathy gives space to, and understanding of, our situation — without compounding it.

Some external environments also can be very undermining to our spirits and are best avoided. Places that are crowded, smokey, confined or noisy can be detrimental, and it is a good idea to get out into fresh air, sunshine and a natural environment as often as possible. Being exposed to Nature uplifts the spirit.

Part of our home environment includes the kind of music we listen to and the books we read. Listen to music which inspires rather than depresses. Read books about people who have overcome so-called insurmountable obstacles in their lives. When we look back at history, the people we revere are the ones who, faced with an obstacle, manifested the wonderful human spirit which says, 'I'm going to give it my best shot anyway'. It is that spirit which lives on and inspires others. Television rarely provides any real nourishment for the spirit, so discriminate in what you view. One of my New Year resolutions for the past two years has been that I won't seek entertainment which scares me half silly or depresses me. My preference is for movies and theatre which inspire or make me laugh!

FAMILY CONFLICT

Occasionally I meet a situation where either the spouse or family don't agree with the treatment sought by the patient. This can be very stressful and depressing for the patient who, no doubt, has thought long and hard over their decision. It can also occur when the patient has had enough of treatment and the family still want them to continue. When I was diagnosed with leukaemia and was told I wouldn't see Christmas, my father was keen to send me to the 'best' specialists anywhere in the world. I had already had the 'best' of what the University Hospital in California had to offer. However, he thought maybe there was somewhere else worth investigating. I wasn't keen to go anywhere, as I felt my healing lay in a deeper understanding of myself and the changing of some pretty rigid and long-held negative beliefs. I wanted to be left alone to figure out my best approach and I knew meditation would play a large role in that healing process. For my father, it was extremely difficult, as he was desperate to 'do' something, and it appeared to him that most of the day I was sitting in my room with eyes closed!

It is doubly difficult for the support person because they can't have access to our thoughts unless we make a real effort to communicate with them. Once I had explained to my father and told him how important it was for me to have his whole-hearted support, he became one of my greatest allies. In the long run, it is the patient who must, in conjunction with their doctor, choose their own treatment, as this is part of taking full responsibility for their healing and their life.

CHOOSING YOUR HEALING PROGRAMME

There are many healing modalities available in the community which fall outside the spectrum of traditional medicine. It can be confusing to the person newly diagnosed to know which ones will be worthwhile and which ones will offer no real benefits. The main areas to look at are:

Relaxation, visualisation and meditation techniques
Nutrition — including juices, vitamins and other supplements
Exercise
Attitudinal healing

Relaxation, visualisation and meditation techniques

These techniques are the most important to the person with a life-threatening disease; indeed, they are important for everyone. Meditation, in particular, is perhaps the first and most important technique in establishing a healing programme. Its value cannot be overestimated. It is the foundation on which a consistent experience of peace can be built. It empowers our decisions about positivity in our lives and strengthens our belief in the other modalities we may have chosen for our healing.

Nutrition

I don't believe there are any magic diets which work for all people. I have worked with patients on many different diets over the years and have not seen any consistent results. We read about people who believe they healed themselves through carrot juice, through grapes, through raw beetroot juice and so on. When one looks at the common factor in all these cases, one finds an unshakeable belief in the chosen diet and in the patient's ability to affect the outcome of their disease.

I believe a diet rich in all the essential nutrients for the body is generally the most acceptable. There are many factors involved in finding the appropriate diet for a patient, such as the state of the digestive system, the support available to them in the preparation of food, their cultural background or religious restrictions, personal preference and emotional equilibrium. It is because of these considerations that it is advisable to find someone who is competent and experienced at designing such a diet, so the patient feels completely confident in its application and effectiveness. This same ruling applied to juices as well as vitamin and other supplementation. In addition to the diet, vegetable juices can be enormously beneficial, and yet in some instances of colonic cancer or chronic diarrhoea in AIDS patients, it is inadvisable. For this reason there is no place in this book for a blanket-type approach to nutritional needs of people with life-threatening diseases. It is essential to work with each patient as a unique being, taking into account their physical condition, their emotional state, their spiritual needs and their psychological make-up. No two patients are following the same path. Each must find what is appropriate for themselves. Timing is always important, and what may be inappropriate today may be the perfect answer tomorrow. A responsible therapist can be of great benefit in sorting out what is most helpful.

Exercise

Exercise should be enjoyable! Find exercise which is pleasurable whilst giving your body what it needs. Ideally you could work towards twenty minutes of sustained exercise daily, which gets your heart pumping and increases the depth and frequency of your breathing. Again, this will be a very individual thing. For those confined to bed, arm exercises or isometric exercises will be appropriate whilst for others it may include working out in a gym with weights. Exercise is not only beneficial to the body, it enhances our feeling of well-being and can certainly lift our spirit. Your exercise routine can be gradually increased as you experience the benefits and ease of consistent practice. For some, group activities like tennis, squash or basketball fulfil other needs for companionship and team spirit. It is great to feel part of a group of people who are practising what you are endeavouring to achieve — abundant health and vitality. Work within your own limitations and don't set unrealistic goals for yourself.

Deep breathing is another excellent form of exercise and is often overlooked. Begin to notice *how* your are breathing. Often you will find that your breathing is a reflection of how you are thinking. Depressing thoughts are very evident in a sagging or stooped posture. This posture restricts our breathing and this has other consequences. If the mind is full of positivity and enthusiasm for life, again, our posture reflects it. Our shoulders are comfortably in relationship with an erect spine and the head is held high; our breathing then is full and deep. Become aware of your own breathing patterns and start to explore the difference regular breathing makes. First thing in the morning is a great time to practise ten to fifteen minutes of deep breathing, preferably outside with bare feet in contact with the earth. Breathe in peace and harmony, vitality and enthusiasm, and breathe out all resistance and tension. Laughter is one of the best and most enjoyable forms of exercise. Invite funny friends over. Hire videos or go to movies which make you laugh. If you find something to smile about, then escalate it to a chuckle; if you find something to chuckle about, escalate it to a good laugh; and if you find something to laugh about, escalate it to real rip-roaring belly-laugh. Laughter is infectious. It is the one infectious thing you should go out of your way to catch!

Attitudinal healing

Although we have covered in this chapter many of the things which will assist us in gaining and maintaining a positive approach to life and our healing, another chapter, 'Techniques for Living', will deal with the specifics involved. Often we have long-held beliefs and attitudes which cause us stress or unhappiness and in this chapter we explore ways in which we can let go unwanted patterns and create new ones which lay foundations for greater peace and harmony in our lives.

Once we have established a programme which feels comfortable and appropriate to our needs, we can relax and fully enjoy our healing journey, trusting healing is taking place and all is unfolding just as it should. Healing is a creative act in answer to your own positive efforts. During the healing process there will be times of willing, and times of surrender, times to push against resistance and times to flow with the river of life. The aware person learns to listen to the still small voice within to gain the understanding of what is essential in each unfolding moment. The dance of life is unique for each person. One cannot learn it from a distance or from a textbook. One simply needs to listen to the soft rhythm within and begin to move.

Chapter Two

Making Decisions

There are many decisions which need to be made as you progress through the process of healing. In the initial period of shock and disbelief the mind tends to be scattered and will clutch at any straws. Well-meaning friends and relatives can sometimes increase our confusion. Suddenly our home is transformed into a library of books and tapes on healing our particular disease. Everyone seems to know someone whom we *must* talk to or see. The more we read, the more bewildered we may become. Our greatest enemy is confusion. It undermines all good intentions and makes us feel powerless. Sooner or later, one comes to the realisation that *you* are the one this is happening to and *you* must decide what is best for yourself. No-one else has your particular disease; no-one knows just how it feels to be you, right now.

You may need to make decisions about who is the right doctor for you. Do you require a second opinion? Is the doctor you've chosen likely to be a person in whom you have confidence, and with whom you feel comfortable? Which other therapies do you wish to investigate? Where do you begin? Which diet will you adopt? Which meditation technique? So many questions. Often there is an underlying feeling of urgency which compounds our bewilderment. Fortunately, there is a useful formula for dealing with the decision-making process.

THE DECISION-MAKING FORMULA

This formula has many applications. It can be used in almost every situation. Tailor the formula to *your* particular requirements, but keep in mind the principles set out here.

1 Make a date with yourself for the decision to be made. Allow a suitable length of time to gather and assimilate your information.

2 Find as much information as possible about the subject on which you need to make a decision. Talk to others who have had experience, read books, research which facilities are available in your community and which provide the necessary or relevant information.

3 Let this information gradually distil inside you. Use some of the time after your meditation to 'tune in' to what is truly helpful to you. Remember, within you there is the absolute knowledge of how to bring about your healing. You only need to find the right combination of things to establish the perfect environment for that healing to take place.

4 Make your decision on the date previously decided and make an absolute commitment to the course of action you have chosen.

5 Trust completely in the decision you have chosen, believing it to be the perfect one for yourself at this time.

6 *Believe* that healing is taking place right now.

7 Set a period of time wherein you wholeheartedly implement your decision.

8 At the end of this period of time, evaluate your progress and make any adjustments or additions which appear necessary.

9 Maintain your programme whilst listening to the voice within. This allows flexibility in your decisions.

10 Repeat steps 7 and 8 regularly.

For some people the decision making process is quite new and unfamiliar — and these are *major* decisions being made. So, for those people who have difficulty in this area, be gentle with yourself and concentrate particularly on trusting you have made the right choice.

Many people complain they feel powerless to affect their illness because they have handed over the responsibility of their healing to their doctor. By using the above process we can take back the full responsibility for the treatments and therapies which *we* decide to utilise. We employ the expertise of our oncologist, immunologist, naturopath, nutritionist or whatever, rather than following advice blindly. It is never wise to make a decision out of fear. By following the formula given, we feel we have taken back full control over what happens to us. In this way, we can orchestrate our healing team.

New choices will present themselves along the way. New books, new therapies, new ideas from other patients. Learn to listen with your heart as well as your discrimination so you can ascertain which things will be of benefit to you.

When we take responsibility for our lives and our health, we emerge from the quagmire of confusion into the crystal clear light of certainty. Once the necessary decisions have been made, act as if those benefits are already on the way to you, trusting implicitly. Believe you *have* the very best doctor in the world; the diet you have chosen is the perfect one for you and for your state of health; your meditation techniques are designed specifically for you and all the support, encouragement and benefits are already being experienced.

Many people, acting out of fear, have travelled all over the world, forever seeking some new therapy or clinic which may benefit them. In the beginning it is a good idea to spend time assembling information on the therapies and therapists with whom you feel comfortable and in whom you trust. Once you have done so, it is essential to knuckle down to the implementation of those chosen therapies and trust in the healing taking place.

To be constantly changing therapies or therapists suggests the right choices were not made in the first place, or the person making the choices does not trust their own ability to discriminate wisely. Peace of mind is our greatest healer. It must become our primary goal. Feeling clear and comfortable about the decisions we have made is essential to having peace of mind. Some decisions which you will need to make may also have drawbacks attached to them — for instance, chemotherapy or any other toxic drug treatment, radiotherapy and surgery.

Some diagnostic tests have drawbacks attached. If you have decided, after going through the decision-making formula, that the benefits of your choice outweigh the drawbacks, then make a firm commitment to concentrate on the benefits and minimise any of the side-effects. Sometimes even drawbacks can be turned into positives.

Occasionally, in the middle of the night, I used to get drenching sweats from my waist up to the top of my head. At first I lay there thinking I was quietly dying whilst everyone else was sleeping; not a very happy thought! For my sanity, I decided to visualise the sweats as my excess white blood cells rushing out of my body. In this way it became more than tolerable. There's a great expression, well worth remembering: 'Would you rather be right or happy?' My visualisation certainly may not have been founded on scientific truth, but it definitely increased my feelings of 'I'm OK'. If you have decided on chemotherapy as your best avenue of treatment, then visualise that liquid pouring perfect healing light into your body, filling it with vitality; the light so strong that any old or diseased cells wither away to be replaced by vibrant, energetic and healthy ones.

Techniques of visualisation and affirmations can certainly be used with great benefit to empower our decisions, and we will expand on them more fully in a separate chapter.

Chapter Three

Stress and Relaxation

'She's *killing* me as surely as if with a knife by her non-co-operation.'

'I'm sick to *death* of this diet.'

'My life is so *deadly* boring.'

'When I didn't get straight A's my father sulked. I just wanted to *die*.'

These are some of the more gripping, yet poignant, comments which I have heard over the years from various people with life-threatening diseases. Note the terminology used!

Much has been written about stress in recent years. It is still a controversial subject. Many doctors disagree with the premise that stress can cause disease. However, more and more doctors are becoming interested in the theories about the connection between the mind and the body. A new branch of medicine has even sprung up to describe this new way of looking at health and disease. It is called psychoneuroimmunology. Broken down into layman's language this means that what we hold in our minds — our thoughts, attitudes, beliefs and feelings — have a direct and indirect effect on our immune system via neurological pathways. Perhaps one of the reasons this new branch of medicine is so controversial is because it means our immunologists also have to have knowledge of the mind and its role in creating health.

In this chapter we will look at some of the physiological responses to stress and then the more specific application of stress and relaxation in the lives of people with life-threatening diseases. Throughout the history of medicine, the recognition of the part the mind plays in a patient's recovery has always been acknowledged. In this century, particularly since the discovery of antibiotics, medicine has taken a more technologically-based view of disease. In fact, medicine is now primarily learned by studying disease rather than exploring the ways in which health is gained and maintained. There was a time when every doctor knew that the basis of good health was contentment and peace of mind. When a person was subject to overwhelming stress — either through grief, depression or continued discouragement — it was considered to be the breeding ground for disease.

Within the last fifty years or so, we have gained immense technological skills which often have their application in the field of medicine. The effective drugs which have given us the power to manipulate and control some diseases, have tended to make it easy to overlook the relationship of the mind to the body. Instead of concentrating on what ingredients create abundant health, we, as a society, have focused on how to alleviate disease. Patients often walk into the doctor's room wanting a piece of paper with a prescription written on it. Usually, they do not want to hear advice about their lifestyle. The attitude of the patient is very much 'Let me do what I want, and you fix up the consequences'. Whereas technological advances and new drugs can be subject to scientific means of appraisal, it is much more difficult to measure the effectiveness of a positive and enthusiastic attitude on the regression of a disease.

There was not a great deal of ideological difference between traditional medicine and 'alternative' or 'complementary' medicine in the early part of last century. It is since the advent of drugs and technological advances that we have moved away from consideration of the mind's potential to influence the health of an individual.

This difference is rather well demonstrated when we look at the life-cycle of a virus or bacteria. There are several essentials which must be available to the virus or bacteria in order for them to reproduce. One of these necessities for reproduction within the life-cycle is a suitable host. It seems it is at this point that 'traditional' and 'alternative' therapies diverge. Traditional medicine concentrates on the elimination of the 'enemy'. This elimination may take the form of surgery, drug therapy, radiation and so on. The art is in finding what will eliminate the disease without eliminating the patient! Some wonderful drugs and techniques have been discovered in this way. Our skills in surgery are extraordinarily refined, as are many other areas of medicine.

Complementary or alternative medicine concentrates on

increasing the health, fitness and well-being of a person so they are vibrantly healthy in mind, body and spirit and would therefore also be an unsuitable host for any virus or bacteria. Health is not just the absence of clinical disease. Health is a dynamic state of being.

When we truly love and care for ourselves, we can expect vibrant health to follow. Through our behaviour we can gain a clear image of the extent to which we respect and love ourselves. To talk about self-love may be a new or strange concept to some people, because it is a very misunderstood term. Over the years, anything with the word 'self' in it has become suspect, as in 'selfish'. To consider, and put self first, is regarded as unacceptable.

One of the commandments in The Bible is 'Love thy neighbour as thyself'; so we have from the highest source that we are to love self and, in fact, it is necessary to love self in order to be able to love others. By your actions you will be able to see to what extent you love and respect yourself. If you don't eat healthily what does it say about yourself? If you smoke — what does it say about yourself? If you don't get adequate exercise — what does it say about yourself? If you burn the candle at both ends — what does it say about yourself? If you fail to take prescribed medication — what does it say about yourself? If you fail to wear a seat belt when driving a car — what does it say about yourself? These situations illustrate how the conscious mind has interpreted what is being felt or understood by the subconscious mind. What these actions are saying is either, 'I am', or, 'I am not, important enough to take care of myself'.

Many people give out very mixed messages. On the one hand a patient may have lung cancer and be doing many really positive things to improve health, by taking vitamins, exercising, improving diet and so on. And yet, they have only managed to 'cut back' on smoking, when really it would have made better sense to stop entirely.

One woman, who was suffering with AIDS, was very keen to assist herself in whatever way she could. She was eating a really healthy diet, taking vitamins and working out several times a week in a gym, and yet she 'couldn't' give up smoking. She told me it was a form of compensation for all the 'hard' disciplines which she felt she had inflicted on herself. Clearly she had chosen these 'improvements' in her diet and exercise programme not out of a sense of love and care for her body but because she thought she *should* do them if she really wanted to stay well.

Whilst the examples such as those mentioned above are open to change through our conscious choice, there are unseen and more subtle effects of this lack of selflove. The body is influenced by the thoughts which the mind holds. In some ways our mind is very like a computer and it will only deliver in the way in which it has been programmed. It can only retrieve the information which has been fed into it. If the subconscious mind has only ever received messages of a negative, self-demeaning nature then those are precisely the messages which will flow out to every cell within the body. This happens via our nervous system. It is unrealistic to expect the body to be healthy and run smoothly whilst the mind is full of depression, grief, despair or thoughts of unworthiness. If, silently in our minds, we have thoughts like 'Life's a struggle, I can't cope', 'I just don't have what it takes to meet the standard', 'I'll never be good enough', 'I'm so stupid, everyone else understands', then it is obvious every cell in the body is going to feel the stress of such thinking. It matters not to the body whether this thinking is in the conscious or subconscious mind. It will still have its influence.

I believe, in time, it will be found that people who have a chronic problem with low self-esteem, or who feel a 'failure', or who suppress anger, or who feel deeply discouraged and daunted by life, secrete into the blood-stream chemicals and hormones which suppress the immune system. These hormones and chemicals, I believe, will be identified as the same ones which we secrete when we are under physical threat. This response to a physical threat is essential to our body's health when we are required to make a physical effort.

Back in the days when we lived in caves, we were frequently faced with physical threats to our lives. If a bear appeared in the mouth of our cave, our bodies had a distinct and essential physiological response. Instinctively, we pumped powerful hormones and chemicals into our blood-stream, which had a whole range of effects on our bodies. We immediately became very alert; our rate of breathing increased so we drew in more oxygen; our rate of expelling carbon dioxide escalated as our respirations quickened; the heart-rate and blood pressure increased as did the blood flow to our arm and leg muscles. These responses enabled us to either fight the bear, if we considered our cave worth defending, or to run like mad — reassuring ourselves we were fortunate to have escaped so easily! If we chose to tangle with the bear, then our bodies were equipped as well as possible for that task. Likewise, if we decided our best chance lay in escape then we also had the right internal environment to allow that to happen. In either case there was a great deal of physical activity.

This physical activity uses up the effects of these hormones and chemicals, and so the body is returned to its usual physiological equilibrium. After the extraordinary stress of the impasse with the bear we could sit down and inspect our injuries and, if we had been successful in fighting off the bear, reassure ourselves. 'There's no place like home'. Or, if we chose to run, we could enjoy the respite from stress whilst cogitating over where to find another cave for the night.

The problem with this marvellous mechanism, known as the 'fight or flight' response, is that it can become activated by stressful situations in which the answer is *not* intense physical activity.

A friend of mine has two magnificent black cats, half Burmese, and a source of great pleasure to her. The animals are well cared for as their gleaming coats testify, and are surrounded by every luxury. They are sisters but are not similar in any way except their colouring. One cat is plump, relaxed and sleeps a lot. The other is jumpy, nervous, even a trifle neurotic. Both cats as kittens were the same playful bundles, but as they grew up they were exposed to stress. Next door to their home, a building was being demolished and a new development commenced which required the use of heavy earth-moving equipment and pneumatic drills, with continuous noise and vibration. Both cats were terrified by the noise but their manner of dealing with their stress was startlingly different. As soon as she had her breakfast — at precisely 7 a.m., when the noise started — the plump contented puss retreated under her mistress's bed for the entire day. The other cat walked around the apartment all day with a haunted look, unable to sleep and looking over her shoulder all the time in case there was a bulldozer in pursuit. She began pulling her fur until, from the rear, she looked as though she was wearing moth-eaten pants. When the cat was taken to the vet, he explained she was suffering severely from a hormonal disturbance due to the stress caused through the turmoil next door, and he prescribed for her. Here in the animal kingdom we have a demonstration of how these two cats dealt with the 'fight or flight' response. On the one hand, the plump puss retreated to a safe environment and 'tuned out' whilst the mistrustful moggy suffered damage to her hormonal well-being by her inability to fight the situation or find any suitable mechanism, whereby she could cope.

Other familiar situations which trigger this response are: a motorist cutting us off in the traffic; a policeman pulling us over for exceeding the speed limit; someone unfairly criticising our highly prized child; the neighbour who insists on burning off what seem to be old tyres on our washing day; the fact that *he* didn't take out the rubbish for the hundredth time this year; that *she* nagged about the clothes on the floor in the bedroom yet again. I'm sure you have your own frustrating favourites. All these examples, and I'm sure your own, make us grit our teeth, tense our muscles and make our heart beat a little faster. If this is compounded with a poor self-image, depression or feelings of failure or entrapment, then it is a very likely possibility our fight-or-flight response is permanently left 'on'. In fact, we can become so accustomed to the stimulating effects of these stress hormones that, should they ever decrease, we almost deliberately go out of our way to re-establish what to us has become the 'normal' equilibrium. Many of us only 'feel alive' when our stress chemicals are flowing. In this way we educate our bodies to believe being stressed is 'normal'. It is rather like having a stimulating drug circulating in our bloodstream all the time. It wasn't until I was sick and investigating the patterns of behaviour in my life that I was able to identify this tendency. I realised that I 'thrived' in the midst of a crisis. If there wasn't one around, then sure enough, I would create one.

This tendency was evident in much of my behaviour. One

common example was my habit of procrastination. Many people thrive on being pushed to their limits and will create the situation in which they are pressured by time. We do this by leaving things to the last minute and then get ourselves into a flap, trying to accomplish, in a short time, what we originally had lots of time to complete. One of the long-term effects of these chemicals and hormones circulating in our bloodstream is the depression of our immune system's response.

The immune system is extremely complex in both its components and functions. Simply put, its function is to recognise what is 'me' and what is 'not me'. One of the functions of the white blood cells is to recognise foreign cells, like bacteria and viruses, and to recognise imperfect cells. When it does find these cells — the 'not me' cells — it sends out for the scavenger lymphocytes who are then mobilised to dispatch the 'foreigners'. I do not mean to oversimplify the complexity of the immune system. It is incredibly intricate and wonderful, quite awesome in fact.

This knowledge gives us tremendous cause for celebration. There is so much we can do to co-operate with our magnificent immune system. We just need to provide all the essentials, and then trust it is performing its task perfectly. This means controlling what we hold in our mind so the body only receives positive, encouraging and loving thoughts; that we affirm this thinking by giving our bodies the best and freshest foods and other substances for its health; that we exercise and rest the body adequately and we lift and inspire ourselves frequently through the use of meditation.

Through the regular practice of physical relaxation and meditation we allow the body to find its own chemical equilibrium. The hormones and chemicals created through stress subside and the body comes back to its 'resting point', where it experiences an internal stability — often referred to as homeostasis. In the chapters on meditation and visualisation techniques we will explore more fully the techniques to assist in the process of re-establishing the body's homeostasis.

Chapter Four

Techniques for Living

There is a lovely story which comes from India about a man who was travelling from one town to another. As he entered this particular town, he stopped at the well to refresh himself. Sitting by the well was a very old man, and the traveller said to him, 'What sort of people live in this town?' The old man looked at him and asked, 'What sort of people did you find in the last town you visited?' The traveller replied, 'Oh, they were a fine people; full of warmth, hospitality and kindness.' The old man nodded and said, 'Yes, you will find the people in this town very much like that also.' The traveller bade him farewell and went on his way into the town.

Shortly after, a second traveller passed by the well and, likewise, said to the old man, 'What kind of people live in this town?' The old man replied the same way as before, asking what kind of people he had found in the previous town. The traveller replied, 'Oh, they were a mean and inhospitable bunch of rogues. I didn't feel safe for a moment.' The old man nodded again and replied, 'Yes, I'm afraid you'll find the people of this town much the same.'

The story illustrates perfectly how our perception of things dictates exactly how we will experience events in our lives. When we look at the world through the glasses of victim-consciousness, then rest assured the events we draw to ourselves will all be seen in the light of this perception. It is not always an easy habit to change, especially when we have a disease which debilitates and frightens us. I well remember the panicky feelings which assailed me whenever I had the thought that there was some kind of monster running rampant in my body. Initially these thoughts were accompanied by a feeling of total powerlessness to change the situation.

A life-threatening disease has a hidden advantage. Although you can feel 'stuck between a rock and a hard place', all the old solutions either don't have any appeal any more, or they simply don't work. If we have always suppressed our feelings, have presented a facade of 'I can cope', and try to continue this attitude when we are diagnosed, we may very well compound our problems. In fact, practising old solutions may well have contributed to your poor state of health.

About five weeks after I was initially diagnosed, I started to really take stock of myself. Up until then I thought the diagnosis was incorrect and there was no way I could die — I just didn't feel as sick as that. Five weeks after diagnosis I began to think they may be right, as I experienced more weakness and inability to do the simplest things without complete exhaustion. At about this time I took to my room, not wanting to talk to anyone, and began to look deeply inside myself. At this time I was qualified as a naturopath, a yoga and meditation teacher, and had been a strict vegetarian and meditator for fifteen years. In fact, it was downright embarrassing to have cancer when I had been teaching others about health!

Through the introspection at this time, I began to see that in my entire life I had not given myself one ounce of self-acceptance. Life had always felt like a real struggle and great efforts seemed necessary even to survive in the world. Ninety-five per cent was five per cent less than acceptable. This applied to every aspect of my life. As a child I was a gifted pianist and yet, when I had an exam 'looming' where I knew I would get less than ninety per cent, I became sick and was therefore unable to sit for the exam.

School, and being a teenager, were two insurmountable obstacles in my mind. I didn't feel I had the mental, emotional or physcial equipment to cope with them. This led to my leaving school just after I turned thirteen. I had many problems with my legs, and, as I had several operations over the ensuing years, I never returned to school.

Clearly I didn't sit down to consciously figure out ways of making my body sick to achieve some underlying motive. Later in my life I didn't think, 'Ah yes, a good dose of leukaemia with a short prognosis is just what I need right now'. And yet, I firmly believe, at some very subtle level, the particular disease and prognosis were precisely tailor-made for me. By this time in my life I was already adept at using my body to manifest illness as a coping mechanism. And, like a lot of people, the six to eighteen months before diagnosis were particularly stressful, with the death of one of my brothers and separation from my husband.

During this time of introspection, many long-held attitudes and beliefs gradually became clear and I felt as if I had painted myself into a rather uncomfortable corner. Some of these beliefs and attitudes had developed as techniques for survival. Even though I had strong spiritual beliefs, I still basically felt life was a struggle. No matter how hard I tried I could never quite measure up to my own high expectations. I grew up believing we were meant to be 'nice' all the time, at all costs. To feel anger, resentment, hatred (a word never mentioned in our home), let alone express those feelings, was the same as throwing mud-pies at God. It was just unthinkable. I have been amazed, since, at just how many other people have had a similar way of looking at the world.

Because of my perceived need to keep all my feelings firmly under control and deeply surpressed, I lived more fruitfully in my mind. If the most important thing was to be a likeable person, then clearly the 'bad' feelings would have to be kept locked up and only the 'good' ones allowed to get an airing. Perhaps, if I only displayed the 'good' ones long or often enough, I could fool everyone (maybe even myself?) that those were the only ones to which I was prone. Deep down, the conflict bubbled and fermented. Perhaps the last straw was the break-up of my marriage, and the death of my much-loved brother.

To believe our bodies can be humming along healthily whilst our minds are full of grief, depression or thoughts of failure, defies common sense. How can we possibly have a well-functioning and enthusiastic immune system if our minds are full of fears, self-criticism and harsh judgements?

A life-threatening disease has the possibility, if we are willing to allow it, of showing us how we have lived our lives up until now, and it gives us the opportunity to assess and decide if that is how we wish to continue. For myself, it was obvious that much of my thinking and attitudes were enough to make any immune system turn up its toes. If there has been an underlying thread right throughout my life, it has been a great desire to understand. To understand the whole mystery of being here. How and why people get sick. Why we make the choices we do. How the intricacies of the entire universe come together to create perfect balance and harmony. Why humans have the extraordinary capacity to make choices. Choices in thinking, in actions, in expression of feelings.

It is often said, 'People don't change'. I believe that statement is only made by people who do not welcome change in themselves. It is what sets humankind apart from animals. We have complete choice over the kinds of thoughts we wish to hold in our minds. What a tremendous point of power!

In the shower, fairly early in my illness, I was devasted to see so much of my long, thick hair going down the drain. It really felt as if it was *me* going down the drain! My tears mingled with the water of the shower. One day, the thought occurred to me that I could experience the water flowing down over my body as a powerful torrent of healing light. It could flow right through my body, bringing energy and vitality to every cell. Just a simple change of perception. And yet, even though simple, one frame of mind was the antithesis of the other. One set of thoughts brought depression and a distinct feeling of powerlessness, whilst the other brought a sense of hope and positivity.

We cannot always change the outcome of a disease but we can certainly change the way in which we experience that outcome.

When we make a firm commitment to life and to experiencing our connection with the flow of power and love in the universe, extraordinary and unexpected events begin to unfold. Greater peace, equanimity, and joy are experienced even in the midst of disease and the experience of these qualities creates the perfect environment for healing to take place.

There came a time in my illness when I felt so lacking in energy that I wanted it all to end right then. Not in a few weeks but right in that moment. I didn't want my children to see me going through what I perceived as degrading, undignified scenarios which surround serious illness and death. Surely a phone call saying 'She's gone' would be preferable.

Obviously, this thinking was still at a time when I felt powerless to affect the course of my disease at all. During this time I prayed earnestly every night, *not* to wake up in the morning. I was still panic-stricken because I didn't feel I had any control over my life. Perhaps I could have control over my death? Even this was denied me! So, again, I needed to look at my thoughts and see what could be changed. The beauty of being 'stuck between a rock and a hard place' is that it forces us to find new ways of being. The old habits and patterns don't work and we seek new ones.

After a time I took to a changed little ritual as soon as I awoke each morning. I would visualise Jesus Christ sitting on the end of my bed. In my mind, I thought Christ knows more about healing than anyone I'd ever heard about. So I concentrated all my attention on Him. I would reflect on His life, His qualities. I guessed there were many times, in His life, when He thought, 'Do I really have to go the whole way? Couldn't I just slip away quietly, resume life as a carpenter or something?' His never-give-up attitude; His gentleness; His acceptance; His lightness and sweetness; His commitment to truth. Then I would visualise these qualities as light which radiated from His body. When I used every ounce of my concentration I could see that light extending out to fill the whole room. I could 'see' it surrounding my body and I would begin to breathe in its radiance. Each inward breath, drawing more of those qualities inside my body, inside my mind. No matter what state I had awakened in — be it pain, discomfort, depression or despair — within minutes I would begin to feel the peace of Christ, the presence and healing power of Christ, and it would always change my perception of how things were. In this way, I would survive each day. Throughout the day, and when assailed by fears in the night, I would wrap myself up in a coccoon of His light and presence, and feel comforted. It is a practice which I have continued. It is a way of 'handing over' my perceptions to a greater power outside, or deep within myself. It doesn't matter that perhaps, I just have an overactive imagination. If it brings comfort and hope then I would rather experience those qualities than despair and powerlessness.

This technique can become almost second nature after awhile. Oftentimes I will visualise I am sitting inside the body of Christ whilst lecturing or talking with a patient. This has led to some unexpected experiences — unexpected both for myself and for the person I am talking to. Intuition seems to increase manyfold.

Some time ago I was working with a lady, Elizabeth, who had cancer of the liver. I was seeing her once or twice a week for several months and we would talk and I would give her a massage. Elizabeth was Jewish, and, although she was not attending her synagogue regularly, her religion was very important to her. Elizabeth had only been given a very short time to live when she was originally diagnosed. After some months of a changed diet, juices, vitamins and meditation she was declared in remission. She was still fearful of the cancer's return and much of our talking was around her anxieties for the future. We seemed to have hit a spot where she wasn't deteriorating or improving. She wasn't sick, but neither was she entirely happy. On one particular occasion when visiting her, I finished the massage by placing my hands over her liver, one hand below her body, the other above. I visualised I was standing inside the body of Christ and let His hands be my hands. As the minutes passed, my hands became hotter and hotter and they almost felt as though they were glued to her body. Afterwards I asked Elizabeth what she had experienced. I was amazed to hear her say that she had had to open her eyes at one point, because she was certain that Christ had His hands on her and she had been filled with great peace and the certainty that she was loved by God. She finished by saying what a strange experience it had been for her as she didn't have any relationship with Christ.

These experiences are still mysteries to me and I make no claim to have a profound understanding of the mechanics involved. All I *do* know is that these techniques bring comfort and, for some people, a new perception of their life. Elizabeth continues to experience a deep and fulfilling peace in her life and the fears, once held, have dissolved.

When I was sick I knew if I continued my negative, self-critical thoughts, then surely I would die. If I practised these other techniques the outcome was certainly open to other possibilities. Even if I were to die, the peace and sense of hope these techniques gave were clearly going to make the experience of dying as comfortable as possible. I never claim to have cured myself. My quality of life now is certainly much better than before I was diagnosed, because my level of self-acceptance, self-love and respect is much greater. I am in remission, and I expect to remain so for the next fifty or sixty years. The important thing is not how long we live but the quality of every day lived. Question the quality in your life:

Did I have fun today?
Did I feel challenged and fulfilled by my work?
Were my interactions with other people genuine and satisfying?
Were my actions full of integrity?

These are good questions to ask yourself on a regular basis. If you see, from your answer, that there is room for improvement, look into why you have dissatisfaction and feel free to find more appropriate ways of living your life. This is the only life I am currently aware of living. I definitely want to give it my best shot. In that way, I expect the future will take care of itself.

To change the way we view the world may seem a lot to ask, especially at a time when we are already under considerable stress. We need to find other ways of looking at life because the ways we have been using up till now may not be helping us. They may even have been causing the very problems we now wish to overcome. We can be fearful of letting go habitual ways of thinking or doing things. Sometimes I felt it would be easier to end my life rather than to let go a cherished way of thinking. In a way, I knew I could 'do' a good death, but I didn't know how to 'do' a good life!

However, little by little, I began to let go and trust. It even became fun as I explored new ways to 'be'. Meditation and visualisation techniques formed the basis on which these changes began to take place. I found I didn't have to be the same person anymore. Life became an adventure. Rather than thinking my way through this process, I concentrated on 'feeling' my way. I enjoyed feeling the early morning sun on my body; I enjoyed *feeling* the flow of warm light-filled air into my lungs, rather than *thinking* it would be 'healthy' thing to do.

Instead of thinking what would be good and healing for me each day, I started to 'feel' what would be good for me. Gradually my language changed to include far more 'feeling' words than 'thinking' words. The mind is mostly preoccupied about the future, or chewing over the past, whereas the body always exists in the present moment.

When we bring the attention of the mind to the experience of the body, we are more easily able to enter the realms of feeling.

Exercise

Try an exercise for a moment.

Concentrate all your attention on the little toe of your right foot: not thinking about it, but actually *feeling* your little toe. You may need to move it a little to locate it fully in your mind. Notice its temperature, the texture of your sock or the pressure of your shoe, or the touch of the air. Bring all of your awareness to your little toe, right now.

You probably found, when you did that simple little exercise, the mind became still and receptive to sounds around you, to atmospheric temperature, to the soft touch of the air against your skin; an overall awareness of your immediate surroundings. This experience is not dependent on your thinking processes, but on your feeling ones. It has a remarkable capacity to clear the mind of any thought. This very simple technique, of focusing our attention on the sensations in our body, can give us the opportunity to let go unwanted or undesired thoughts and can help move our reality to more neutral ground.

Everything in our culture is geared to overload our senses and our mind with information. To actually stop, listen and feel is a totally new experience for some people. It embodies the beginning of meditation. It can become quite intoxicating in its effect, and can lay foundations for a new way of experiencing life. This way includes a freshness and spontaneity so often lacking in our lives. It connects us with each unfolding moment — each one new, never to be repeated; each one precious and full of potential. The heart understands these words easily. The mind questions, tries to distort, attempts to complicate. The mind thrives on activity. It has been described by Indian teachers as a wild, drunk monkey swinging through tree-tops! The heart is still by comparison. Learn to trust its stillness and in the knowledge which arises out of that stillness. Allow yourself the luxury of peace. Learn to value it as your most precious asset.

With this attitude it is surprising how many worries take care of themselves and dissolve back into quietude. When panic or anxieties assail you, just put them on 'hold' and spend some time with the techniques of relaxation and letting go. If they are important concerns or panics, rest assured they will be there for your attention later. Don't fight them off. They are like wayward lost children who are tired and irritable and they clamour for your attention right now. Like overtired children, they need reassurance and putting to bed. Having done that, practise being at peace, practise trusting that everything *is* alright, that everything is unfolding in its own perfect time. In the beginning, it may seem an insurmountable task. Fear makes its presence known. Reassure the fear; put it to bed. And practise peace once again.

Some people find it helpful to develop a little ritual around these fears or panics. Perhaps you could visualise putting them into the basket beneath a hot-air balloon and then, loosening the ropes, letting it soar up and away. Or, literally, bedding them down and simply turning off the lights. Or seeing those fears surrounded in light, melting away into that light. Find something which seems appropriate for you. Perhaps some method which jumps out from your own lifestyle.

One man, a gardener, used to visualise these unwanted thoughts going into the compost heap in his back garden. Another lady, who had a swimming pool, would visualise all the heaviness of these thoughts being washed away as she swam through the water each day. Find whatever seems to be appropriate for you. If you have any affinity with Christ, you may wish to use the technique mentioned before; visualising you are sitting inside the body of Christ, letting His love and light protect and heal you of your fears. Further techniques for visualisation are given in the relevant chapter. These techniques can extend to healing relationships which have caused us pain.

Healing Relationships

We often believe, mistakenly, that a painful relationship from the past is best forgotten. Yet, more often than not, it isn't forgotten: the painful memories are just buried deep down inside ourselves. We may say we don't wish to be reminded of the pain it caused us. But the fact is, it is still causing us pain and we are therefore still in relationship with that person. The person may no longer be physically present in our lives. Yet their influence is still there. Quite likely, at the time of being hurt, we made some 'laws' about how we would henceforth live our lives. Laws like:

'Never trust men' or 'Never trust women'
'Don't let anyone in too close or they'll hurt me'
'I'd better make sure I get my needs met first, otherwise I'll lose out'
'Never trust a stranger'
'Mediocrity is safe'
'If I am not too ambitious then I can't fail'

Have a look at which ones you have created for yourself. When there is someone in our life who has hurt us — even though that person may now be dead — we remain in relationship with them. It is as if there were a rope stretched between that person and ourselves. We are still holding on hard to our end of the rope. When we let go our end, it sets free a lot of energy previously trapped by negativity held in that relationship. We may need to 'let go' that rope a hundred times before we are successful in totally forgiving the person, situation or our actions within that situation. We can then learn from the experience and move on. Many people have no desire to forgive those who have hurt them in the past. We can almost savour our hurts as avenues for us to feel righteous indignation. To let go the resentment or bitterness also means to let go the righteous indignation.

By forgiving the past, we can cultivate compassion for others, the compassion which we would like to have extended to ourselves. We all make mistakes. Recognise them as opportunities to learn something new. They are there for our education, not to carry around with us for an eternity. Acknowledge the resentment, forgive the person or situation, accept it, and move on. In this way, we continue to grow. Held resentments and bitterness cause stagnation.

FORGIVENESS

A technique of forgiveness we frequently use in our groups is to sit quietly and visualise someone for whom we have love. See that person in your mind's eye, and allow all the love and warm feelings you have to flow out to that person. Enjoy the experience. Then let the image of the person fade away.

Now allow the image of a person to whom you feel quite indifferent come before your eyes. Perhaps it is someone like the girl in your local paper shop, the postman, or someone with whom you are not closely associated. Visualise the person strongly, and again allow your love and compassion to flow out to that person. You may find it is quite a strange experience for you, but persevere. Just allow warmth and kindliness to flow out from your heart to that person. Then, in your own time, allow the image to fade and replace it with the image of the person who has hurt you in the past. Again, see the face clearly before you. Notice what is happening in your body, and let the tension soften. Visualise that person, and allow whatever love and forgiveness you are able to muster to flow out from your heart to that person. If you find it difficult, that is alright. Allow whatever understanding and compassion you have for that person to flow out from yourself. You have been angered or hurt for so long, just let it soften and melt into light and ease. Your natural state is love. Even though it may be very difficult for you to feel any truth in the following words, try them anyway: 'I forgive you for all the things I thought you did; in word or thought or action. Please forgive me also.'

If it is easier to start with people or situations which are less threatening for you, then do so. The important thing is to keep practising. The day will dawn when you will feel only light and love flowing out to that person, providing that is what you desire. You can see, by the resistance to forgive a person, how much energy is bound up by that relationship. This energy, when it is set free through forgiveness, is truly amazing. Energy, now liberated, can be used for your greater healing.

Sophie and her husband took an extended holiday, leaving the running of their business in the hands of their partner. On their return, they were dismayed to find the woman had mishandled funds deliberately in her favour. The business foundered, and it was left to Sophie and her husband to make restitution to a number of creditors. This left them penniless at a time when unemployment was rife and the skills of her husband were not in demand. They slowly began putting their life together again, but Sophie, in particular, had deep-held feelings of resentment and bitterness toward their former partner. There were also deep feelings of anger. About eighteen months after the breakup of the business, Sophie developed cancer of the breast. For two years she underwent various forms of treatment. The tumours from the primary cancer spread throughout her body affecting the bones, lungs and liver, and these secondary growths caused her great pain.

It was at this point she joined one of our support groups. She became a very regular member of our group and it became obvious that this previous incident still dominated much of her present outlook. Sophie shed many tears in the group over her anger and frustration and, in time, it became clear to her that to maintain these feelings held her back from healing and increased her pain. When it became obvious to her that she needed to release the past and to forgive her former partner she sat down to write her a letter. It was a painful and difficult letter to write, yet she persevered. She made several attempts and finally brought to the group the letter she intended to send. In her letter, Sophie had asked the woman to forgive *her* for having held such resentment for all those long years. Through the process of looking and re-looking at the situation, she had come to realise that it was she, Sophie, who also needed forgiveness. Forgiveness for having held this woman in such a bad light for all that time. Sophie recognised that when we hold resentment and bitterness in our hearts it becomes a poison which harms us. She felt genuine remorse in having held these feelings for so long. She sent the letter away, feeling entirely relieved and saying she didn't need to have any reply as it felt complete for her.

However, very soon, a letter arrived from the woman who also poured out her grief and sadness over the past situation and asked also for Sophie's forgiveness. This letter was stained with many splotches from tears. It was amazing to see the transformation which took place for Sophie. Her face softened and she became much more accepting of herself and others. Interestingly enough her pain level also dropped significantly around this time.

ANGER

Some people are easily able to transcend their anger through the techniques of meditation and forgiveness, while others need to find suitable outlets to really get their emotions moving. There is nothing negative about experiencing anger. It is a natural emotion. What *is* negative is to keep the anger inside where it can only fester and cause injury to the body. Anger can change the chemical balance in the body and is certainly detrimental when not discharged. These chemicals are the same ones which trigger our 'fight or flight' response. To let your anger flow out is an excellent way to get emotions moving and circulating in your body. In this way you 'use up' the effect of these chemicals. It can be difficult sometimes within our suburban environments to freely express anger without causing neighbours concern or at least raised eyebrows. It is inappropriate to express our anger through physical violence, but there are many excellent ways of 'getting it out' without offence to other members of society.

Expressing anger

The following are a few suggestions for physically expressing anger which won't cause damage to yourself or someone else.

You may find, because this is a very unaccustomed way for you to behave, that initially you feel self-conscious, or a bit foolish. The mind will probably jump in and say things like, 'I'm not really *that* angry about Aunty Flo throwing away my favourite teddy bear. It was so long ago now, it doesn't really matter', even though at the time you may have been outraged at her actions and frustrated by your feelings of powerlessness. Persevere until you really get in touch with the outrage within. This exercise only works when you can really put your belief into what you are doing. If you are beating a pillow with your fists, then you must believe the pillow *is* Aunty Flo. It is often very hard for people to get into this type of exercise without supervision and assistance. Hitting Aunty Flo isn't what we are really doing. It is just a means by which we can belt out the anger towards her, and often it is the image of the person which can stimulate the rage. Basically we probably love Aunty Flo dearly. It is the anger we still hold around her actions which we're ridding ourselves of. By using these techniques, the potency of those emotions can be accessed and freely expressed. Another excellent way to express anger is to beat the earth with a stick — or to beat the blankets or carpets on the clothes line with a broom! The important thing is to really put your belief into what you are doing.

When all the emotion of anger is spent, there are usually tears of sadness mixed with relief; a feeling of release and deep contentment; a sense of having passed through the storm rather than having just skirted its edges; a sense of completion.

It is not until we have access to the subconscious mind that many of our negative, fearful or long-held attitudes become apparent. The subconscious mind is what really dictates how we will react to a situation. Our subconscious mind is that part of our awareness which 'remembers' every past experience and has made 'personal laws' or rules which filter all future actions and thoughts.

GUILT

The most destructive, useless and stagnant energy of all is guilt. It paralyses our actions and achieves nothing. It brings only oppression and fear: fear of punishment. To feel guilt presupposes we believe we have committed actions not acceptable to the mores of our society. If we believe we have erred, it reinforces our sense of unworthiness; that we are somehow not acceptable as we are. If we have done something for which we feel shame or are genuinely sorry about, then let there be remorse. Honest remorse comes from the heart, not from the mind. Once we have felt, acknowledged and apologised for what we did, if appropriate, we can learn from it and go on enlightened.

For many years I felt a terrible guilt because I believed we were meant to be perfect and I knew I wasn't. I tried so hard to maintain an image to the world which said, 'I know who I am; I know where I am going; I am a capable, efficient, intelligent person and everything is just fine.' However, I felt a fraud and a hypocrite, knowing none of these things were true. It was far from a happy way to live. On the outside, I tried to maintain the image of coping with everything, while on the inside there was a constant voice of self-criticism: 'You spoke too long; too short; too loud; too soft; you probably confused people; you're making a mess of everything; you're just not good enough!'

It has taken a lot of determination to not only become aware of this negative, self-defeating tendency, but also to stop doing it! For some of us accomplishing self-acceptance is a life-long task. Believing we are somehow worse than everyone else is exactly the same as believing we are somehow superior. 'So you think your heart is full of imperfections — huh, you should see mine!'

These days I tend to go to bed with the attitude, 'Oh well, I made a few more mistakes today. I'm sorry, especially if I confused anyone. I might have spoken too loud, too soft, too long or too short.' Of course, we're going to keep doing some or all of these. Being aware and more accepting of myself helps me to be able to say, 'Anyway, I'll be out there tomorrow doing my best.' And instead of any self-criticism, I go to sleep with a peaceful heart. I feel more responsible for my life and my actions, and yet I don't feel the weight of the world resting on my shoulders, or that the 'bogey man' is out to get me. Self-acceptance makes self-forgiveness unnecessary. It 's O.K. to be human. It's O.K. to make mistakes. In fact if we don't acknowledge mistakes, we would just go on making them. When we take total responsibility for our actions we are free to leave the darkness of guilt and to move into the Light. Guilt is negative and keeps us bound while responsibility is mature and liberating.

BLAME

It can be easy to blame others for the predicament in which we find ourselves. This exemplifies 'victim-consciousness' and needs to be eradicated from our whole being if healing is to take place. It is easy to feel victimised and, at one time or another, we have all felt so demeaned. Blaming others is the antithesis of taking responsibility. Thoughts which we hold in our minds will dictate the reality we experience and it becomes our choice as to what we wish to hold there.

One man, Angus, who is in his early fifties, had to give up his work as a lecturer in statistical analysis when he was diagnosed with cancer of the oesophagus. He underwent extensive surgery and was quite debilitated when he first came for help with his nutrition and meditation needs. There was so much anger and frustration in him, and it seemed quite pointless to discuss anything before addressing his immediate state. Angus was having a very difficult time adjusting to early retirement. It meant he and his wife were thrown together in a far more intense way than they had ever experienced before. His wife, Gillian, also found it a great strain to 'have him around home all day watching how I do things'. Angus felt if only his wife would do things the way *he* liked them to be done, or in the way *he* would do them (inferring, of course, that this would be the right way) he would be able to get well. In his view, she was killing him by her non-cooperation. This extended from how she washed the dishes, to how she answered the phone, to keeping the kids quiet whilst he 'furiously' meditated!

If any healing was to take place in this man, it was clear it must begin within the family, and within the attitudes, before any change would even be worthwhile contemplating in his diet. To talk about vegetable juices at a time when serious injury might be inflicted by the juicer in flight, would be totally inappropriate. Furthermore, he could hardly drink juice through his clenched teeth! The only sane course of action in this situation was for the couple to seek professional counselling to help sort out priorities and means of communication, plus some techniques for relaxation and meditation. My concern was equally for the emotional and physical state of his wife.

It is interesting to look at what was behind Angus' behaviour. He felt there was something going on in his body which was out of his control. Being a statistician didn't help. Numbers move along very prescribed lines. In his mind, he had decided that if he couldn't control what was happening in his body, then he would control (to within an inch of his life) what was happening in his outside physical environment.

People may use blame for many different reasons but each and every one will come back to not wanting to own their responsibility. Society re-inforces this attitude in many ways. We blame the weather. We blame 'circumstances'. We blame other people. We can even blame society. We go out of our way to avoid taking responsibility. When we accept our responsibility it means we decide to make changes in our lives. If we continue to blame outside circumstances, what we are really saying is, 'If only *you* would change, I would be happier'.

Change is often resisted because it is new and unfamiliar. We adhere to old routines even if they make us sick. If it were not so, we would all be eating perfectly healthy food in just the right amounts, exercising regularly, thinking peaceful and harmonious thoughts, and stepping out into the world with boundless confidence and enthusiasm to meet all the challenges which come our way. Certainly a lifestyle of personal reponsibility opens the way to greater health, peace and vitality.

Taking Responsibility

Taking responsbility for our actions increases our feelings of self-respect and self-worth. Perhaps get someone to read this exercise to you. (To be read very slowly.)

Close your eyes for a moment and visualise some act or situation for which you feel a lot of guilt. Really let the feeling which goes with that activity or situation become strong in you. Notice the effect on your body. How does your heart feel? Your shoulders? What is happening with your breathing? Is it an experience of lightness or of heaviness? Let all the feelings associated with that incident come into your awareness.

Now focus on your heart, the constriction felt there. Introduce the soft presence of Light, self-acceptance, opening up around the darkness, breathing in Light, and easing the pain. Letting go the tightness, letting it be soothed and eased by the soft light flowing in on your breath. Releasing the pain of remorse into the soft cleansing presence of Light.

When we are dealing with taking responsibility for our health and the treatments we choose, it means we will be informed to the best of our ability and understanding about both our disease and its treatments. Your doctor is clearly the most knowledgeable person to speak to you of your disease and its processes and of the medical treatments he can offer.

If we can accept that primarily we are souls who are embodied rather than bodies who happen to have souls, then it can give us some meaning or framework in which to create our healing.

I believe the universe is entirely ordered and that no thing happens haphazardly. Leukaemia was the best thing that every came my way because I learnt much more about myself, more quickly than I could have without it. This experience of illness has been restated many times by others who have viewed their disease and healing process in this same way. The areas in which it is necessary to take responsibility when we have a life-threatening disease involve the establishment of peace of mind. To have peaceful and harmonious thoughts; to acknowledge and release past hurts, angers, resentments and feelings of unworthiness; to ensure the body receives all it requires for abundant health and healing. When we can cultivate an overall feeling of life being a game, or fun, and learn not to take it all so seriously, it makes the heart lighter.

Once, when I was sick, I was given a rose. I dissolved into tears because I thought that this was probably the last rose I would ever see. Then I had the thought this was also the most beautiful rose I had ever seen and if I just enjoyed it being there now, there was nothing more I could wish for.

When we have taken one hundred per cent responsibility for how we conduct our lives, how we think, how we feel, then we learn to trust. Trust that healing *is* taking place, trust that everything is unfolding just as it should, trust that if healing occurs in mind and spirit but does not include my body, then that must also be alright. To achieve this state of mind takes considerable effort, as we so much want healing to be done on our terms. If we view cancer, AIDS or death as a monster lurking over in the corner, and we desperately seek ways to 'buy him off', we are generally not successful — especially in achieving peace of mind. When we learn to trust whatever happens to us is for our highest good, it can give us the courage to look at disease, death or negativity and make really fundamental changes to the way in which we look at life. Once I had looked at death and all the parts of me that were so scared to live, I was better able to deal with those aspects of myself.

To affirm life in every way — through relationships, through thoughts, through the healthy expression of feelings, through diet, through exercise, through laughter, through facing challenges — is to create the perfect environment for healing. For the rest, we trust.

BARGAINING

Many people approach the various healing modalities with the underlying attitude that 'If I'm good enough, if I meditate deeply enough, long enough, if I never miss a juice, if I take all these vitamins and herbs, if I exercise, if I pass the test by doing all these things, then maybe my reward will be that I get well.' This bargaining attitude stems from fear. The same old fear of 'Maybe I won't be good enough'. The fear of a standard which I have to meet and yet, don't think I have what it takes to meet it. It is not an easy thing to do, to trust all is well. When we are willing to change, to embrace what is new and unexplored, life can become an adventure. To continue with the old criterion of 'Do I have what it takes?' is to perpetuate a pattern all too familiar to some of us. Remember, a lot of us are high-achievers and we may well fall into the trap of finding a diet or other programme so rigorous that it could almost make failure a certainty. Don't misunderstand me. I am not saying diet, even rigorous diets, are not beneficial. What I *am* saying is that the attitude *behind* the diet is of paramount importance; the attitude *behind* the practice of meditation is of paramount importance.

A lady once flew across the country to consult with me. She had cancer for three and a half years and knew more about diets and clinics for cancer patients than I did. She had travelled extensively in search of a cure and was very fearful. For three quarters of an hour she spoke of her medical history and the treatments she had undertaken. Her doctor had told her she had only a matter of weeks to live. Her entire day was governed by the clock. She was taking more juices, vitamins and other pills than you could find in a health food shop, and her diet was made up of completely raw foods. She said, 'I'm sick to *death* of the diet and all the pills but I know they are my only hope.' Notice her choice of words!

This lady understood many basic principles, but only on a very superficial level. We talked about the foods she was missing and all of them seemed to be quite innocuous. As the interview proceeded, I was becoming more and more uncomfortable, wondering what I could suggest to her that she wasn't already doing. That was the key. *Doing*. This lady had 'doing' down to a fine art, but had not ventured much into the land of 'being'. She was meditating, and enjoying it, but it too, was done for a prescribed length of time each day. The 'prescription' I gave her that day might sound quite ludicrous to most people — especially to other naturopaths! I suggested she throw away the clock; eat and drink whatever she felt to be beneficial; meditate to her heart's content; stop taking all tablets (she wasn't on any medical treatment); that she spend time each day listening to the music she enjoyed; and that she go to the Children's Hospital in her city and offer to read in the Burns Unit.

She began to weep, and a long story about her inability to have children came out, along with many other disappointments in her life. She returned home and followed the recommendations. Over the following months I received several wonderful cards from her. The last time I heard was eighteen months after her initial visit. She was still going from strength to strength and was organising other volunteers to go into the hospital. She still had tumours, but they no longer pre-occupied her.

This story illustrates perfectly the need to have an individually tailored programme which is appropriate for each person. Had she been on chemotherapy or other treatment, the advice would have needed to be quite different. Her chief problem was that she had focused entirely on herself and she needed to release the past, enjoy the present and begin to give love and attention to others. Her determination, placed in a healthier direction, was all that was needed. If she had one ounce less tenacity, she wouldn't have come for help in the first place. Nor would she have followed the advice given, especially as she was seeking more things to 'do' rather than the suggestions she received.

DREAMS AND THEIR INTERPRETATION

Our subconscious mind is what fuels our dreams with their images. In our dreams many unresolved problems are played out, so it can be very beneficial to work with someone who is familiar with interpreting dreams to help us gain a better understanding of our present situation. If you choose to do this, it is necessary to write in detail all the aspects and information contained in the dream. Even if you are working only on your own with your dreams, the process of writing them down can be very helpful.

KEEPING A JOURNAL

Keeping a journal can be a wonderful way of getting in touch with your deeper thoughts and feelings. Not so much a journal of events and happenings in your life, but a record of how each day unfolded for you at a 'feeling' level. This is also a valuable way of uncovering 'feelings' about things rather than 'thoughts' about things. Reactions to conversations, people, situations, or events can be noted. This journal is invaluable as a tool for discovery about yourself. Even long after you're well, you will continue to learn much about yourself from its pages. To share your journal with a trusted loved-one can also be beneficial, and can provide a base for further discussion.

DRAWINGS

Much has been written in recent years about the value of drawings as a means to access the subconscious mind. I have used drawings extensively with adults and children with life-threatening diseases and they have provided valuable short-cuts to understanding the innermost feelings of the patient. What we can acknowledge and express through our conscious minds may be completely different from what we truly feel in our innermost being. It is impossible not to give away what is happening in the subconscious, when we draw. This applies even if we wish to cover up what is there. One of the values of drawings is that it puts something 'out there' for us to discuss. Unless we gain access to these hidden feelings which empower our actions, choices and decisions, we continue along in our habitual way.

I usually ask a person to draw pictures of themselves, their tumours or disease, their white-blood cells, their treatment, their family and any other drawing of their choice. Sometimes I ask the person to draw themselves and their family when they were a child of five, or to draw any other relevant relationship which may seem fruitful for exploration. Many people complain that they can't draw. This in no way inhibits this process. It can even enhance it, because what we *do* put down on paper will not be contrived. The only 'rules' for drawings used in this way, are:

white paper
crayons or coloured pencils — no felt tips
a wide range of colours to choose from
no stick figures

Sometimes we will have a drawing morning within one of the support groups and we will each work on another person's drawings. These mornings are enormously valuable and enjoyable.

Colours

Colours are a valuable indicator of how a person perceives their situation. This applies not only to colours used with their drawings, but also colours in which they dress, or decorate their homes. To deliberately change the colours around us to uplifting and cheerful ones can have a marked effect on how we feel. If you are someone who habitually wears subdued or sombre colours, try wearing some other harmonious but brighter colours, just for a change.

Music

Like colour, music can lift the spirit and brighten our day. Choose music *you* find enjoyable. If music represents a fairly new adventure for you, then take note of what you enjoy on the radio and perhaps purchase copies for your personal collection. Don't be shy about going into a whole new area of music.

If your only musical world has been popular music up until now, consider investigating your likes and dislikes in classical music. Likewise for those steeped in classics, investigate jazz or popular music. As with all things, there is no one right way or, in this case, no one right music. You enjoy what you enjoy. Be liberal in your investigation. You may surprise yourself by what you *do* enjoy. Just as there is not one right music, so there is no one way of listening to it. I have enjoyed popular music with a very strong beat through headphones as I worked out on a rebounder (a mini trampoline) and I have experienced classical music whilst in a deep state of meditation. Part of the time during my recovery I was living in a very large geodesic dome in the foothills of the Sierra Nevada mountains in California. A large part of the dome had been replaced by glass and the outlook was straight over the mountains with not a house, light or road in sight. In the evenings it was possible to lie on the floor of the sitting room and stare straight up into the heavens with the myriad stars twinkling in the clear night sky. I would put on a selection of music, turn out the lights, stretch out on the floor, allow myself to melt into the carpet and give myself over to the music's influence and surrender totally. In this way I did not experience the music through my intellect. It almost felt as if my body became an instrument also, and the music was played 'through' me. Just letting the notes play through me, rather than making sense of them with my mind, was a powerful experience. It felt rather as though my consciousness had become a vast ocean in which these vibrations rose and fell, ebbed and flowed like the waves. So, allow the limits of your musical enjoyment to stretch. Be open to new forms of music and new techniques of listening.

In this chapter we have touched upon several avenues and techniques which you may wish to explore further. There are many others. Each person finds their own healing, in their own time. As has been stated often, there is no one right way; there are as many ways as there are people. Learn to trust that you are moving along your path of healing at your own perfect pace. Be open to new possibilities, new ways of doing things. Add them in to your programme if they appeal, and trust that all is unfolding perfectly for you.

Sleep

Anyone who is unwell has an increased need for sleep. And yet, it is at this very time when sleep may be disturbed or elusive. We may need to implement correct sleeping patterns if they have become disarranged through hospitalisation, pain, worry, or some other factor. Healthy sleeping patterns may be re-established by implementing a sort of ritual around bed time.

The worry of *not* sleeping can, of itself, keep sleep at bay. Lack of sleep is nothing to be overly concerned about. We can catch up. Remember, a good day's worry is more exhausting than a good day with an axe. This applies doubly if we are going to spend our nights in fruitless worry. Everything seems worse at 3 a.m.!

So begin to affirm, throughout the day, that you will have no difficulty at all in falling asleep easily when you go to bed. Every time you are assailed by the thought of another sleepless night, gently put it aside. You will probably find it best not to watch any stimulating dramas on television or read any riveting books. It is generally best if you do not eat immediately before bed. A warm drink of chamomile or valerian tea can help to relax and calm the body and mind. If feasible, a warm bath in the hour before you retire can also be very soothing. Some people benefit enormously from a herbal formula which calms and relaxes the body. There are some good formulas available through your health food store. These usually contain L-Tryptophan, as well as sedative herbs. The sleep achieved through these herbs can be deep and refreshing. On the other hand, the medically prescribed sedatives may have side-effects which you will find difficult to deal with. Many people complain that they don't wake up refreshed after using prescription sedatives.

The use of a relaxation tape as you settle in to bed can be helpful in getting the mind focused and the body relaxed, allowing sleep to come as it will. I have made a tape for people who have a chronic sleep problem. The use of this tape can help to re-establish healthy sleep habits, or it can be used occasionally when there is anxiety or physical discomfort. It is available from the address in the back of the book. No-one has ever heard the end of this tape!

SELF-ESTEEM

Many people who develop cancer or AIDS have a real problem with self-esteem. Of course, we are not the only ones in society who have this problem. It is all too common. We somehow prefer to put people down rather than build them up. We may do this with our children too, unless we are watchful. If our self-esteem is low, its effect will be felt in every part of our lives. Many of us with cancer excel in one area of our lives, and we may work quite hard to convey the image of being equally successful in all aspects of our lives.

Where does this crushing need to be perfect come from?

Is it from childhood where our best efforts were never quite good enough; where parents berated us instead of encouraging us?

Perhaps as we came to adolescence and had demeaning nicknames thrust upon us — 'Fatso', 'Squirt', 'Dumbo' or whatever. We longed to be like the popular, good-looking members of our class or school, not realising that they, too, probably had their hang-ups and uncertainties. Perhaps our low self-esteem came from a father who, though a 'good provider', and therefore in the eyes of the world a 'good father', was always at meetings, out to dinner and never at home when we longed to talk to him about what was happening in our life. What may this tell us? That other things were more interesting, more worth his attention than being with us? Perhaps it was not long before we got the message — I am not important, I am not interesting, I am not worthwhile.

A broken relationship where a lover has rejected us, may translate into 'Men don't like me' or 'I am not attractive to men' or 'I'll never have a husband' (or their equivalent counterparts). Sure enough, the subconscious programmer gets to work and this is what we begin to project.

I remember overhearing two teachers talking about me when I was about eleven or twelve. One was trying to describe me to the other, who didn't know me by name. She said, 'Oh, you know the one. That mousy-haired, sickly-looking girl'. It was like a dagger to my heart. The fact is, maybe they weren't talking about *me* at all! Maybe it was my sensitivity being 'out there' looking for confirmation that I wasn't up to scratch. But I certainly 'owned' what was said. Sadly our projected images of ourselves are so powerful that, even if we want to, they can be extraordinarily difficult to change. These images inhibit our reaching out to others, developing our skills, building relationships, embarking on careers.

Our personalities can become corroded and we may never realise our full potential. We go on giving out negative estimations of ourselves and people take us at our face value — the value we have been at pains to project even if deep down we know we are 'not really like that'. This further builds our 'victim-consciousness' because we also get into thinking 'Why can't they see what I'm really like? I must be the way people *think* I am'. This self-perpetuating circle brings more and more pain. It often leads to a break-down in our health. However, often out of break-downs come break-throughs.

Many people have said they are grateful for their illness because with it has come insights into themselves, previously unsuspected, and they come to realise with joy that 'I'm not so bad after all'. At one stage, it occurred to me that to think I was somehow worse than everyone else was just the flip-side of thinking I was better than everyone else. 'You think you're unworthy; well I'm much more unworthy than you!'

So what can we do about this sick kind of thinking?

A good place to start is in our choice of words. We would all benefit by leaving out the words:

can't (usually means won't)
but (looking for an excuse)
if (wanting it to be different from how it is)
should (who says?)
ought (who says?)
impossible (start thinking 'possible')

When we look back through history at the great people who continue to inspire and uplift us, they were not the kind of people who would have used any of those words. Imagine if Beethoven had said, 'If only I wasn't deaf, I'd keep writing music'! Or if the Wright brothers had decided after their first unsuccessful attempt that it was impossible for humans to fly . . .

We each know people in our own lives who have inspired us to go beyond our usual limitations. Listen to their vocabulary.

You will find it is full of positive statements. They are usually powerful people who have the capacity to create what they want in their lives. For those with a religious background, incorrect application of the word 'humility' can be the start of low self-esteem. Humility is not self-belittling and yet it is sometimes interpreted that way. Often this attitude is carried with a person after they leave their Church. We have been told 'to love others, as yourself'. This certainly implies we must honour, respect and love ourselves if we hope to be able to do so for others.

We can renew ourselves by consciously taking opportunities to do things we enjoy — going to a play, a concert, a film. Take time out to watch the waves on a beach, a sunset, sunshine on new leaves — surround yourself with uplifting things.

Check also to hear when we are putting ourselves down. And stop, even if it is in mid-sentence. Change it to a positive.

Learn to accept and give a compliment. Be open to the love others extend to you and return it in full measure. Take every opportunity to listen to, and help others — even if the help seems minimal. Right motive makes the degree of help irrelevant. It is the desire to help that often heals.

Our self-esteem is helped as soon as we start looking outwards instead of inwards. When we are less self-absorbed by our faults and practise giving love to others by being genuinely interested in their welfare, our life begins to take on a richness and depth not previously felt. After a time, we don't need to consciously 'practise' this, because it becomes second nature to us.

Positive imaging can bring our desired goals very close indeed and give us confidence to go on believing. There is much information on this aspect of positive imaging in the chapter 'Visualisation Techniques'. Be prepared to give up your unrealistic expectations of yourself or others' expectations of you. This is *your* life. It is not a dress-rehearsal. What you are living now is the real thing, so feel challenged to take the risks which come with changing your way of thinking. Understand that you don't have to be 'saintly' perfect. You're perfect and acceptable just the way you are. Give yourself permission to make mistakes. Celebrate your mistakes as a valuable means of learning something. A so-called mistake then takes on a new meaning. If you have acknowledged that there is a better way of doing something then you have gained new and valuable knowledge. Self-flagellation is out! Self-congratulation is in!

Love your imperfections as much as the things for which you allow yourself credit, because they are all part of the same you. Stop judging yourself. One cannot release thoughts of negativity through rejection, only through love. So be nice to yourself. And, stop scaring yourself. We spend so much time and money on scaring ourselves half-silly. We do this by watching scary movies, reading depressing articles about our disease, and so on. Create a safe, warm and loving world around you, not one where you perceive attack lurking around every corner. Many people perceive their cancer cells or the AIDS virus as 'out to get them'. Change your perception. Cancer cells are weak, unintelligent cells who have forgotten how to behave appropriately. Love them out of your body. One lady, who had cancer of the liver developed a lot of compassion for her cancer cells. She used to massage that part of her body every day whilst 'talking' to the cells there, telling them help was on the way and everything was going to be alright. They didn't have to panic as she was sending some special healing cells to re-establish the 'right' knowledge these wayward cells needed. The cells she 'sent' to this area were very old and wise. This practice brought her comfort and confidence in her ability to heal herself.

When we realise our life has been one of self-criticism, doubt or despair and that there *is* a better way, it is as if a light has been switched on and we take our first steps out of emotional darkness into our true Self. Then we can be comfortable but not complacent with our imperfections.

To find the Light within ourselves is a wondrous experience, and yet, we cannot find the Light until we have acknowledged the darkness. When we acknowledge the Light in others, our own begins to shine more brilliantly. Trust in your own ability to find peace, joy and self-love. There is no room in our lives for ancient history. Forgive the past, release its influence, and move on. Ultimately, it is taking responsibility for ourselves by dealing with what is causing us pain, ridding ourselves of guilt or any other negative emotion, and proceeding with greater self-acceptance. With self-acceptance comes acceptance of others, and of the events in our lives.

Chapter Five

Support Groups

There is nothing quite so valuable and comforting as to be among people who understand and can empathise with our situation.

A support group, effectively facilitated, creates a safe, warm and supportive environment in which any issues can be discussed with complete openness and frankness. Often there are problems or concerns which we feel unable to share with our families, perhaps because it will be too upsetting for them or they will not be able to respond in any really helpful way. Even though we live so closely with members of our family, it is often said by participants in the group that those closest to them physically don't really know or understand what they are going through. Such groups give us the opportunity to explore and verbalise our innermost feelings and the courage to express them to our loved ones. I have never experienced any difficulties at all in mixing people who have cancer with those infected by the HIV or with AIDS. All these conditions are potentially life-threatening, therefore the needs are the same. I believe there are some benefits in having an AIDS support group run separately because there are some issues around sexuality which may be particular to infection with the HIV. It is really a matter of preference on the part of the participant.

Sometimes people have an unsympathetic home environment where the family may think because one has a good doctor, there is no need for any additional support. This can be particularly seen in homes where the wife is the one who is sick and she has always been the one who has to 'cope' in the family. The family's attitude can sometimes be 'If she looks alright, then she must *be* alright'. This can also be seen with people with the HIV in that often their health is not consistently good. At times when we appear well, everyone else breathes a sigh of relief believing that everything can return to normal again. 'Isn't it great! You're better now.' It is often at *this* time that the full impact of what is happening to us hits us. Everyone goes back to work, back to familiar routines, and we are left feeling everything is *not* alright at all!

Jennifer expressed this very well in one of our groups. She had found a lump in her breast, had immediately gone to her doctor, and within seventy-two hours had had her breast removed. Not surprisingly, two weeks later her husband had returned to work, the children had recovered from the disruption in their routine and Jennifer went to pieces. Sometimes this feeling of devastation doesn't come until two months later, sometimes it doesn't come at all. We are all very different in our reactions. Through the support group, Jennifer found great comfort by sharing her feelings and finding others who understood exactly what she was expressing.

Another man, Tony, expressed these same feelings. Tony was diagnosed as HIV-positive and within two weeks he had a complication in the manufacture of his platelets. This condition lead to bruising, and the inability to clot blood effectively. His work environment was very supportive but was unaware of the infection which lay behind his condition. Tony knew that to tell his workmates he was infected with the HIV would greatly jeopardise both the support he was given and his job. The condition, thrombocytopaenia, gradually worsened and finally resulted in him having his spleen removed. All this, with the extra stress of not being able to be completely open about his health.

Weeks later, when Tony had returned to work, his friends, workmates and acquaintances would cheer him by saying, 'Thank Heavens, that's all behind you now.' Each time Tony's heart would sink, knowing that his health was still open to fluctuations. It is understandable that our loved ones as well as our friends will be relieved when what seems to them the worst is over. However, for us, the 'worst' may not be experienced at the same time, and for some the 'worst' is the living with constant uncertainty about the future.

Tony received an empathetic hearing in the support group and was comforted to find his feelings were understood and shared by others. Tony had actually thought there must be something wrong with *him* and that perhaps he was just becoming pre-occupied with his health. We need to have our fears heard and acknowledged; then we are more easily able to live comfortably with them, or dismiss them altogether.

By continuing to participate in your support group, you make a statement to your family and friends of who you are and what your needs are. In this way they can gain some understanding and respect for your situation. We encourage support people to attend either a support group for supporters, or a general group. Sometimes we have a support person attending a general group without the patient. Perhaps the patient is in hospital, or too ill to attend, and yet the carer is in dire need of support. The groups are always flexible in content. No two sessions within a support group are ever the same. We address whatever issues arise out of each group.

Many who are the least willing to share initially find the most benefit from their group association. The empathy and love generated during the sharing is a powerful and growing thing of itself and a bond which strengthens us to go on. We can gain great encouragement from someone who is further down the track than us and is comfortable and at peace with their situation. People who come into the room dejected and anxious always leave cheered and ready to face whatever lies ahead. There are many in our groups who are in remission after they had been told this would be impossible. They provide great inspiration and encouragement to those who are just starting out on the journey. It is generally surprising to people to find these groups are full of laughter and good humour; there are tears too, and these are freely expressed as the need arises. To have permission from others to have a good cry is invaluable. Very often families don't want to see us cry because it puts them in touch with their own distress.

One young mother, Joanne, exemplified much of this. Joanne had just given birth to her first child when a tumour was discovered in her abdomen. Ten days after the birth of her son, she had much of her large bowel removed, plus one lobe of the liver. Some months later more tumours appeared in the other lobe of the liver and in her lungs. It was at this point that Joanne became very enthusiastic about her chosen diet, meditation, juices, vitamins and so on, but was reluctant to join a support group. She had remained cheerful and positive throughout her diagnosis and treatment. However, it seemed quite clear to those of us closer to her, that it was a front Joanne had carefully maintained as a cover-up for her real feelings. When she finally did attend one of our groups, she stated at the beginning that she didn't really belong with all these sick people and there was no way we were going to make her cry or make her let go of her iron resolve that all was well. At this time, Joanne had been given a very poor prognosis, with only a few months to live. Up until the birth of her son, she had been career-oriented, busy climbing the corporate ladder. She believed that it was what she 'should' be doing. She had a position of great responsibility, yet underneath she felt a 'fraud' and that she had secured the job on 'false pretences'. She had many self-doubts which she constantly struggled to hide.

Eighteen months on, Joanne is a radiant and contented mother who feels free to be the person she is. Her health continues to go from good to better, though there have been many ups and downs in those months. She attends the support group weekly and is brimful of good cheer and enthusiasm. The times when she is fearful or uncertain, she shares with the group, just as she shares the high and happy times. Her emotions are much closer to the surface and she is less guarded against experiencing the 'downs'. She is an inspiration to everyone else and her enthusiasm for life is positively infectious.

Recently, Joanne participated in one of the most gruelling national quiz shows. She underwent chemotherapy on Monday, Tuesday and Wednesday, flew across the country for the quiz show on Thursday, and returned home for more chemotherapy on the Friday! Between herbals, homeopathics and a positive outlook, she was free of the usual nausea associated with her chemotherapy. She even believes it minimised the butterflies in her tummy!

Not only Joanne, but many others, have gained from her experience of cancer. She certainly exemplifies the positive approach. We can make prisons of our lives by living up to the expectations of others — or even what we *think* are the expectations of others. Joanne found through her voyage of discovery that she was climbing the corporate ladder because she thought being a mother wasn't enough by her family's standards. She thought they thought she was capable of much more than just motherhood. When she actually discussed this with her family she found they had no such expectations of her and she realised she had been struggling for years under a misapprehension. All this gradual awakening took place in Joanne through her participation in the support groups, through meditation and through the loving support of her husband. Joanne tells her own story in the case history chapter at the end of this book.

One apprehension newcomers have often expressed about participating in a support group, is that they may meet people who are sicker than they are, or who are dying. This certainly happens in our groups; yet we have found that to face death or serious illness together has been a great blessing and strength to us. I don't believe it is a negative thing to look at and discuss death. In fact, looking at my own death and the process of dying was the turning point for me. Once my fears were acknowledged and dealt with, my strength began to return. If we have a life-threatening disease, then one definite possibility is that we may die. *Not* to look at that possibility can sometimes take an enormous amount of energy which would be better spent in healing. Being open to life also means being open to death. Once death has been looked at fully, or as fully as we are able, we can really get on with living. Once I had accepted the inevitability of my own death, I made a full commitment to life. If I was going to die, I'd do it with good grace, trusting it was for my highest good, for my children's and parents' highest good, even though I could not understand how it could be so, especially as my brother had died only eighteen months before. But, while I had life and breath, I was going to be doing my utmost to live. And I set about finding ways in which I could affirm life.

To be in a group where someone is exploring their feelings about dying can be invaluable as a way of gaining insight into our own feelings. Sometimes we are a little nervous about looking at our own feelings, and to hear someone else courageously exploring theirs can help us. A ritual has evolved with time and experience within our groups when someone dies. We usually join hands, allow our eyes to close and visualise the person who has died, in the centre of the group. Then we acknowledge inwardly or verbally those qualities which were precious to us in that person: perhaps their enthusiasm for life; or their humour; their tenacity; their ability to let go and trust; their determination to understand the process they were undergoing; their supportiveness towards us, or whatever else may have been of value.

We spend some time in silence speaking in our hearts anything which we would like to say to them and we listen for their reply. Then we visualise the person surrounded in light, made whole and at peace by the power of that light. We wish them well on their journey and we thank them for the gifts they have given to us. These gifts add strength to our own endeavours. We take them into our hearts as light to kindle and enthuse our own. Then we release them to whatever is necessary for them to go forward. Yes, there is sadness at the loss of those who have grown very dear to us. Sometimes they have shared more intimately with the group than they have with their own families. And we miss them. And yet their presences can always be felt in the group and we often talk about the gifts, the solutions they found which are valuable also to us. We tend to remember them more with smiles and joy than with depression or fear. When someone in the group dies, our tears are not all for that person; there are always tears for ouselves. Perhaps this will be me in six months, or a year or two. It is partly us grieving for our familiar environment; our uncertainty about letting go into the arms of the unknown.

The presence of these people who have died is a very real influence in my life. When my brother died, he was in Kathmandu — pretty inaccessible to me in Australia. Now he is here, whenever I think of him. I can't hug him or see his smile, yet I feel his smile in my heart whenever I think of him.

When I am with a child with cancer I have only to remember Charlie, a young boy who passed through a similar time, to feel the appropriate words to bring comfort or insight. Likewise with a judge or a coalminer. The fundamental needs of a judge or child are similar — reassurance, compassion, understanding, empathy and above all, the acknowledgement of their unique and magnificent identity rather than their disease. The very basis of the groups is that they support us in living. We are either alive, or dead. *Whilst we are alive, we are living with a life-threatening disease, not dying with a terminal one.* We need support in living through this situation.

The rules which I have found essential for the smooth and effective running of the groups are very simple:

1 What transpires within the group is confidential and we do not talk about anyone or their experiences outside the group unless it is with their permission.

2 We stick with our feelings rather than theorise about things. This means we talk about how things actually are for us rather than seeing the world through rose-coloured glasses. These rose-coloured glasses may be the ones our families would like us to view the world through or the ones we think we 'should' or 'ought' to use.

3 We don't judge or criticise. If someone is feeling 'negative' or depressed, we don't tell them they 'shouldn't' feel that way. To do that would be to negate the person's present reality. It *needs* to be acknowledged before the person can change their perception.

4 We listen a hundred per cent when someone is talking so that we don't disintegrate into several chattering groups.

The form the groups take is as follows. We join hands and the facilitator then guides the group through a brief relaxation and centring exercise, and into a brief meditation. After that, we welcome any new people and go through the 'rules' for the running of the group. It is essential to have a facilitator who makes sure the rules are adhered to, otherwise it can become a pleasant chatting session but without any real effectiveness.

After the rules, we introduce ourselves to each other. This usually consists of giving a first name and any information we may wish. It may include our diagnosis, an update on the past week, what we receive or want to receive by participating in the group, or a particular problem we are experiencing. For some who are shy, a name can be sufficient. Some will say they are nervous and would like to just sit and listen and, of course, their wish is respected. Once these people feel at ease, they may wish to share more of their feelings.

By the time we have completed introductions it is very clear where the needs of the participants are, and these are then addressed in a compassionate and supportive manner. The idea is not to outdo each other in our dramas, but to listen carefully to what each person is saying. Sometimes we need to listen 'behind' what the person is saying. It is a skill which must be developed.

One woman, Melanie, came to the group very depressed. Her depression covered a lot of anger. She had become infected with the HIV through a blood transfusion. The infection so depleted her immune system that she had developed AIDS. A cancer had been detected and she was undergoing chemotherapy to try to halt its progress. She said she did not wish to continue with chemotherapy as there seemed little hope of it doing anything more than extending a miserable life. With gentle probing, however, it became evident that the real problem lay in her relationship with her husband and child. She couldn't bear them seeing her become so physically depleted and, in her view, ugly — through the loss of her hair, her constant nausea, her thin and boney body. The anger and depression which had first been present, gradually ebbed away with her tears. She even managed to laugh a little at herself as she realised she had equated their love for her with her physical looks. By the end of the group she was much better equipped to meet the stress inherent in her condition and had the courage to include her husband and child in her thoughts and feelings rather than keeping her emotions hidden from them. Having these thoughts and emotions acknowledged in the group, and subsequently by her husband and child, enabled her to renew her strength and resolve to continue treatment.

When we listen carefully to what a person is saying, either directly or indirectly, it enables the person to actually *hear* what they are saying and gives the courage to explore and discover their own solutions. *My* solutions are always *mine*. They may benefit someone else also, but ultimately we all need to find our own solutions to the problems which arise in our lives. It is not a case of 'Where there is *this* problem, this is the solution'. A solution, entirely appropriate to one person, will be inappropriate, perhaps, for another.

In the support groups we are given the opportunity to air our fears and apprehensions and perhaps gain another perspective on them. Nothing is more healing than to be able to laugh at something which was once fearful to us but which now has no power over us. There is a silent permission permeating the group, which allows for free expression of whatever emotions are being experienced, be they grief, panic, anger, frustration, depression, regret, sadness, joy, love, fear, guilt, powerlessness and so on.

One lady, Diane, has experienced each of these emotions at one time or another, throughout her association with the support group. Diane was diagnosed with a pituitary adenoma some years ago and first came to me for advice about her diet, supplements, juices, meditation and so on. Although this particular tumour was not malignant, the usual clinical pattern with such an adenoma, if not controlled by chemotherapy, was to expand until it caused severe symptoms and/or death. For some time Diane resisted chemotherapy as she liked to think she could control it without any outside interference — especially any toxic outside interference. After some months it became obvious that some medical assistance was required and she commenced a form of chemotherapy which had rather severe and unpleasant side-effects. Diane had been receiving careful monitoring from her specialist since her diagnosis and it was with his permission that she had delayed her chemotherapy. Because her tumour was in the pituitary gland, it grossly interfered with the proper functioning of her hormonal system and it was considered impossible, or at the least, unthinkable, that she should have a child.

Diane was the impetus for our very first support group to be formed. She had had considerable experience as a co-counsellor at a women's refuge and was already experienced in going beyond the normal restrictions of exploration and expression of emotions. Her health had improved to the point where the tumour no longer showed on the scans, although her blood levels of prolactin revealed that it was still influencing her body chemistry. She was assured by her doctor that it was not the end of the problem with the tumour and she could expect it to return.

It was about this time that Diane began to worry because she thought maybe she didn't belong in the group as she had no 'life-threatening' disease to qualify! Naturally, we reassured her. Indeed, she was an extremely valuable member of the group and her insight and ability to see into the 'heart of things' was of great benefit to us all. Diane has a wonderful capacity to explore her emotions and the kinds of thoughts or attitudes which lie behind them. Her courage has been an inspiration to many others. One person's courage can certainly en-courage others.

Shortly after her comparatively good result from her doctor, Diane voiced her long-held desire to have a baby. Inwardly, she had always thought, 'When I get over this, I am going to have a child'. She consulted with her doctor who advised against it because 'Nobody with her condition, had done that before'. There were serious questions about her ability to conceive, but, within three months, she was pregnant and carried her infant to full-term. Morgan Anthony Potter was born on February 27, 1988. His arrival was without complication and he has continued to thrive. So has his mother. I am extremely proud to be his godmother and it is to him that this book is dedicated. His entrance into the world truly symbolises the spirit behind each word within its covers.

As may well be imagined, Diane's courage and positivity continue to be an enormous inspiration to those who are newly diagnosed or those who are experiencing the ups and downs of their healing process. Before the birth of Morgan, Diane emanated a peace and radiance. His arrival has only increased it. Her insight into others and herself, continues to enrich us all.

OUTREACH

A lot of support flows outside the formal meeting of the group. It is common when one of the members is going into hospital for surgery, chemotherapy or some other procedure, that several other members of the group will telephone or be remembering them in their own meditations. This feeling of being supported by others is tremendously valuable. It is often said by a participant that even in the darkest night of depression or fear, or pain, the remembrance of the group has brought light and comfort.

These outside activities have also extended to the bedside of someone who is hospitalised or sick at home when two or more people from the regular support group will go to them and hold a group for their benefit. In this way, the person still feels connected to the main group.

When we are beginning our formal groups, we spend some time visualising any person who is unable to attend the group that day due to illness or hospitalisation. We visualise them surrounded in light, made whole, content and at peace by the power of that light. We also often send them a 'rainbow'; that is, we visualise a rainbow of light in our hearts and then see it passing clear over the city, if necessary, to the heart of the one who is in need. Many patients have said they have felt an inflow of strength or support at those precise times and have suddenly felt at peace!

When we have a life-threatening disease we can feel useless as far as our capacity to be actively involved in the community. Often we need to give up work, sport, or other engaging activities and it can easily lead to a feeling of being an observer of life, rather than a participator. We can begin to question our value as a human being, especially when an illness is protracted. Participating in a support group can allay those feelings entirely. Often those who are sickest and weakest give more strength and valuable insight into another's dilemma and it is only because of their courage and awareness of their own plight that they are able to do so. It has frequently been said by members of the group that they have never felt so connected to other human beings as they have since their illness. They say they have found a strength within themselves which they have been able to freely share with others, in a way never before possible. When we are able to share deeply with others it brings about a completion and healing within ourselves.

My belief is we are primarily spirits who happen to be in bodies, rather than bodies who happen to have spirits. What we experience in our groups is spirit reaching out to spirit in love and compassion — and frequently humour — to bring insight, comfort and perhaps a changed perception. The depth and strength of the human spirit has the power to show us the flimsy nature of fear. A situation first perceived as terrifying, can, when brought out into the open and looked at in the light, be perceived quite differently — especially with the added strength of others.

There are a few other practical suggestions for the running of these groups. The facilitator will need to ensure that the group stays within the framework of the 'rules'. The groups are not times for swapping recipes, exercise programmes or sharing other information about treatments. This can be done during the tea-break at the end of the meeting. In this way, we stay focused on the intended content of the group. It is equally essential that the group stay within the prescribed time. I have found a two-hour group to be the most effective. In this time we are able to really address the needs of the participants. We usually have a cup of herb tea at the end of the group and this provides the opportunity for more relaxed conversation.

The groups have led to friendships outside the formal meetings and also to shared activities. We have had picnics from time to time, and these occasions give the families an opportunity to mix in an easy social atmosphere. Much recipe-swapping happens at these events! Wives of sick husbands have the opportunity to hear how each is coping. Children are able to share with each other the joys of kite-flying or duck-feeding. When we are sick, we are often limited by our pain or energy level, and yet it is nourishing to the spirit to participate in these activities with others who have an understanding of our restrictions. At the time of writing, we are about to have our first weekend away in the country. Thirty-five people will be participating. Some have cancer, some AIDS, some are therapists who are interested in developing a greater understanding of themselves and improving their skills, some are children — all are friends. We will focus on meditation, massage, hands-on-healing, sharing, drawings, horse-riding, tennis, kite-flying and so on. It will provide an opportunity for the giving and receiving of love and support.

A support group can be made up of two people who are committed to self-exploration or discovery and, indeed, this is how our support group originally began. Diane — mentioned earlier — and I were the first members. There were just the two of us for many weeks, then three, and it gradually increased from there. That original small group was extremely valuable and gave us an opportunity to find out just what were the essentials for such groups. Out of them arose the four 'rules' for the groups. There are now dozens of such groups fashioned along these same guidelines.

When I was the only participant in the support group, I still spent the allotted time in reflection and in sending love and support to those unable to attend on that particular day. In this way an 'energy' was built up. Now Mondays, from 11 a.m.–1 p.m., are set aside solely for this purpose.

Our group grew steadily until it became too big to be effective. As a group we discussed what would be the best solution to the problem of large numbers. The groups at that time were usually between sixteen and twenty-three. We decided to have two groups each week. People gained so much from the groups that instead of halving the numbers, many of the participants came twice a week! The ideal number for a group is somewhere between six and twelve, though this is flexible. We have had some of our most memorable groups with three participants. Even the very large groups have their benefits.

My preference is to hold the support groups in a private and homely setting, as most people find it less intimidating than a clinical environment. This was really illustrated for me when I moved my practice from home to rooms nearby. The group met there also and, almost immediately, the numbers began to decrease. We went back to one group per week, and even though the rules and structure were identical, the numbers dwindled further. It was decided to return to my home for the groups. Almost instantly we were back to large numbers. At home there is an assortment of seating accommodation. It includes lounge and upright chairs, cushions, bean-bags. The atmosphere is anything but clinical. Our groups are structured on a donation basis.

After the group has completed all of its discussion and there are no further emotional 'loose-ends', we have our joke session. This gives us a wonderful opportunity to discharge emotions through laughter. Oftentimes the jokes have an AIDS, oncology or gay slant — other times, just plain funny ones. The joke session has been a great innovation and we are compiling a book of our favourites.

At the end of each group, we close by laying-on hands on any person who is in need. There is nothing mysterious about the laying-on of hands and people always gain greatly from the experience. The person either lies down or remains sitting, if that is more comfortable, whilst the others in the group gather round and gently place hands on the person. Some prefer to remain in their seats and send loving thoughts or healing from there. Those who feel comfortable with prayer, pray silently for the healing of that person. For others, they may prefer to see or feel healing energy pouring through their hands into the body of the other, healing in whatever way is most appropriate. Others will channel love and support. The gentle touch of a loving friend can heal the spirit instantly, and a healed spirit has unlimited potential.

The groups appeal to all ages. The majority of the people I work with are children, teenagers and adults under fifty. It is only occasionally that I work with an older person. The support group is mostly made up of adults under the age of fifty.

I mistakenly believed older people wouldn't benefit from the groups. One man, Enoch, came to visit me with his family. He had several devoted adult children who were very keen to support and assist him in any way. I almost didn't mention the support group to Enoch believing that the exploration of emotions wasn't really what he wanted. Fortunately, I overlooked my hesitancy and encouraged him to attend. We were in for a treat. Enoch became a regular and enthusiastic member of the group and gave enormously of his wit and wisdom. His willingness to express himself emotionally gave many others encouragement to do the same. Enoch was greatly troubled by his lack of energy and it was a comfort to him to know others shared his predicament and were finding their own solutions. He told us many stories of his childhood and early life and drew strength from them himself, as he looked back at his own courage and tenacity.

I visited Enoch a few hours before he died. He had been semi-conscious most of the previous day. As I bent over him, I told him I had come to say goodbye. Immediately, he was fully conscious and, sitting up in his bed, we gave each other a long hug. He asked me to pass on his thanks and love to the group. His parting from this world was made much easier through his participation in the groups.

Enoch taught me much by his resilience and humour. Though he started out in the group being a little shy, it seemed no time at all before he was able to say simply, "Today, I just need a hug.'

If there is no support group in your area, you may wish to approach the social worker or doctor at your local hospital and express the need for one. Most of the major hospitals within the city have such a group. Some of these groups are more educational in their structure and these can be very beneficial also. However, they are quite different from the kind of group discussed in this chapter. You could begin a group yourself by adapting the guidelines set out here to your particular requirements. You may wish to approach your doctor for the names of other people who may be interested in participating, or ask for the co-operation of the social worker attached to the oncology or immunology department. The important thing is: don't be discouraged. A group of two is still a group. When two or more are gathered in the name of Truth and understanding, the spirit and strength of Love are always present.

Chapter Six

Care for the Carers

'Hello Joan, how's Ted?' Those who are the carers, or supporters of those with a life-threatening disease, will understand the significance of those words. Much as we love and care for those near and dear to us who are unwell, we too feel fragile and in need of nurturing. This becomes especially evident when an illness is protracted. It is essential that equal care go into working out a suitable programme for the carer as for the patient.

The unseen, and often unacknowledged, juggling act which must go on is demanding, exhausting and frequently frustrating. The children still have to be fed and supervised, the dog has to be wormed, and who's going to mow the lawn? Not to mention the shopping, the juicing and the endless preparation of healthy meals. In addition to all the usual activities there are the sometimes frequent visits to doctors and hospitals. All this with an overriding uncertainty of the future. Frequently the future represents an anxiety which 'cannot' be discussed and this creates its own form of stress. The patient's illness frequently makes that person irritable and unreasonable, and this is usually shown toward the family more than anyone else. In our support groups it is often said that we, as patients, don't always know what we want ourselves and that makes it very difficult for the support person to know which way to jump. On the one hand, if someone gets us a chair, we can think, 'I'm perfectly capable of getting my own chair, you know' or if they *don't* get us a chair we can think, 'Don't they know I'm sick?'

Vicki had not long turned eighteen and had had a long drawn-out battle with leukaemia. For her eighteenth birthday her parents had bought her a brand new car. She was enormously pleased and proud of this gift and, to her, it symbolised her ability to establish some independence away from home. At her age this was of paramount importance as for so many years, because of her illness, she had been more dependent than most teenagers. As her illness progressed, and she became very frail, it became quite impossible for her to drive the car. Her younger brother, Jeffrey, had just received his 'L' plates and had decided he would maintain and care for her car as she was no longer able to do so. Vicki became very sullen and irritable around this time and particularly so towards Jeff, who reacted angrily to cover his hurt. This marred the whole atmosphere in the house and the rest of the family also became irritable with the strain of the overall situation.

I had been visiting Vicki twice weekly to have a chat and to give her a massage. I, too, was a little puzzled as to why there had been this particular change in spirits with her. However, something happened one morning when I was visiting her that gave us the key. Her brother was outside washing the car and started it up to move it closer to the garden tap. Vicki's body tensed and it was obvious something had upset her, yet, she still tried to conceal it. On gentle investigation it became obvious what was going on inside Vicki. Her thinking may have seemed convoluted, but, bear in mind that someone who is sick has unlimited amount of time to sit and cogitate over things — to blow them out of proportion or to distort them. Vicki believed Jeff was taking such good care of her car because he knew that, very likely, he was going to get it should she die. To his family, and especially to Jeff, his motivations were clear — it was his way of showing she could rely on him to take care of her prized possession until she was able to resume those responsibilities herself. In her mind there were no such honourable intentions. When the family could see this from her rather distorted viewpoint they were able to make some simple adjustments which solved the problem. Jeff had a beautiful key-case engraved with her initials specially made, and instead of him keeping the keys, which he had retained up until this point, he would go to her and ask if she would like him to polish the car for her or turn over the engine, always returning the keys to her afterwards. In this way, the explosiveness went out of the situation and things settled down again to the warm and open family it was before. Also, a little time afterwards, the whole subject of Vicki's fears, concepts and uncertainties about death and dying were shared by the family.

When someone asks you, 'How are you Joan?' are you the sort of person who says, 'Oh, I'm fine thanks', regardless of how you really feel? This reply is alright when you are talking to a casual acquaintance. But when this person is genuinely interested in your welfare, this sort of reply ends the conversation very quickly. What can your friend say if you give such a reply? It is not whingeing or being negative to say something like, 'Frankly today isn't one of my better days. Ted's treatment ends soon and hopefully that will make things easier all round, but really, today I feel a total wreck!' What you've said, in essence, to your friend is that your relationship is significant enough for you to be real with how things actually are. He or she can give you a bit of a hug and say whatever seems appropriate, even though they may not have any particular solution to your problem. Usually, what we count as being really important is that someone actually hears what we are saying and understands. To say 'I'm fine thanks' when it is not so brings down a wall of non-communication. I have always appreciated the kind of relationship wherein I feel comfortable enough with a friend to really unburden myself; when someone has let me hear myself think rather than just giving me their solution for my problem. Ultimately we all need to find our own solutions for our problems and though listening to other people's experiences with similar situations can be extremely helpful, the ultimate solution has to be found by us.

Patients will react in many different ways to the stress imposed by a life-threatening disease. In fact, different days will bring different reactions. For those who have always been fiercely independent it is very difficult to suddenly express their needs. Being unused to communicating their needs, even knowing how to ask for the smallest thing to be done for them, can be very traumatic. In fact, some people simply don't know how to do it. Another common comment in the support groups is that we often have the underlying feeling that if our supporters *really* loved and understood us, they would anticipate our needs, preferably before *we* even knew we had them. Often there is an undercurrent of anger and frustration in the patient regarding the state of things and if there is no appropriate channel for all that pent-up energy it is usually directed at those closest to us. The patient knows those nearest are not going to desert them and it can become a pattern of behaviour that is difficult to break. It can become even more difficult to see behind a person's irritable behaviour when the whole household is feeling the stress of diagnosis, treatments and the ongoing uncertainty.

Almost always, the diagnosis means people are thrown together more than is usual. This can be a strain in itself. Many a wife has had her busy and enjoyable routine turned topsy-turvy by the constant presence and demands of a husband who was formerly working. Even the best marriage can find this a strain. If it *wasn't* the best marriage at the time of diagnosis, some considerable effort may need to be put in to making it better at a time when there are other pressing issues. But there is no doubt that a crisis can also strengthen the bond between people and many in our groups have testified to this, saying they are now much closer than ever before.

More than ever, at this time, the health of the support person is paramount. Who is going to look after the diet, recreation and exercise of the support person unless they do? There are often good friends and neighbours who offer practical assistance and yet people resist allowing such help. Practise accepting their offered help. Let someone pick up the children from school; or pick up a basket of washing or ironing; or let them sit with the patient while you go and have a game of tennis or get your hair done; let them pick up the groceries for you or cook the occasional meal. People like to feel included and of real practical assistance to you, yet it is up to you to allow them this opportunity. Let go of the fierce independence and allow yourself to feel part of a community. Often the carer feels that if they are doing everything for the patient, it is their way of showing their love and concern. Also, that their love can be measured by how much they actually 'do' for the patient. And, yes, that is a valid attitude. However, when some of the practical details are taken care of by someone else, it allows you more time just to be with the person in a more intimate capacity.

We can also fall into the trap of 'being strong for each other', in the belief that if one shows true feeling it may trigger off the tears of the other. There is nothing negative about tears and frequently the most healing therapy possible is the shared tears of a family. It is a release of tension. If there are uncried tears it doesn't mean 'I'm strong', it means 'I do not feel safe enough to be vulnerable' or 'I am not willing to have the other person be vulnerable with me'. The truth is that the emotions are there, but are unexpressed. Suppressed emotions cause a heaviness in the heart and can lead to illness in the body. Just as for the patient, there are some areas which are vitally necessary for the support person to address. There is no reason why the support person should not eat a really healthy and cleansing diet along with the patient, nor should they only make the juices for them. A multi-vitamin, or a formula which concentrates on the vitamins in high demand when we are under stress, is also invaluable. Adequate rest and time for personal recreation is essential so you are in good shape to fulfil the function of the support person. Time out for self-reflection is helpful and, if possible, practise the techniques of relaxation and meditation along with the patient.

When the patient is expressing anger, hostility, sullenness or irritability, try to remember that what is really being expressed is fear, and it is really a cry for help. Insofar as your compassion will allow, try to understand and meet this need in the best way you can.

In our support groups, the carers are always welcome and they gain much by sharing their own experiences and listening to those of others. We also have support groups for supporters, and in this environment much understanding and acceptance is gained. Also, much humour is shared and participants leave feeling less alone with their situation. I believe that it is very often more difficult for the support person than for the patient. It is a demanding role to put aside our wants and needs for the sake of another. This is especially so if this necessity arises in a marriage or family where relationships between people are already strained.

A family or marriage guidance counsellor can be invaluable at this time to help sort out priorities and to establish open lines of communication between members. In this way, we don't just muddle through the situation but can actually gain benefit from a repaired relationship which has the potential to deepen and become more meaningful.

If playing sport, going to a club, attending classes in some area of interest, or entertaining friends has been part of your life up until now, look at ways whereby you can still maintain those contacts even if on a more infrequent and curtailed basis. Ask friends over for coffee (or herb tea!) instead of dinner, or, if your friends offer to bring something, then let them. You can easily say to friends, 'We really miss seeing you and we'd love to spend some time together. Ted's on his special diet, though, so why don't you come around after dinner?'

It's very important to keep up your contacts, especially if you are a carer, and in this way you maintain as normal a life as possible. When two babies are born and one of them has a hole in the heart, which one requires the most love? Of course, they both require the same amount of love. One may require more care, but the need for love and support is the same for both infants. Likewise, in a family where one member is seriously ill that member will certainly require more care and attention but all members of the family still need to feel loved and cared for. This can be difficult especially if the illness is a lengthy one, or requires much hospitalisation. For people who live a long way from their hospital this is doubly difficult. If it is a child who is sick, then special thought must be given to the needs of the other children in the family. Grandparents, aunts and uncles or other loved adults can fill some of these needs.

One of the loveliest things to do with children is to 'wrap them up in a rainbow' before they go to sleep. What child does not love a rainbow — its beauty and magic? I began doing this with my two children when they were quite young (four and seven years of age). My son, Simon, who was four was having terrible nightmares. His father and I had recently separated and he had found the experience to be particularly upsetting. We developed this ritual at night, as a means to assist and give him comfort.

Once Simon was tucked up in his bed, I would ask him to close his eyes and visualise that I was wrapping him up in a cloud of red. As I talked quietly to him about this beautiful soft cloud of red light, I would pass my hand very lightly over the whole of his body several times. Talking quietly about this beautiful, soft light, like a cocoon, I would be gently and slowly stroking him all the while. Then we would visualise the lovely clear colour of orange: the colour of nasturtiums in the sunshine (one of his favourite flowers). Wrapped in a cloud of clear colour . . . still moving the hand gently and softly over his body . . . and so on through the colours of the rainbow.

The yellow of early morning sunshine, or whatever is appropriate to your child's understanding. The green of lush grass. Blue, like the sky. Indigo, the colour of the heavens at night. And violet, the colour of the violet flower. This ritual can take as long a time as seems appropriate to the age of the child. At the end, I would place my hand over Simon's heart and together we would visualise a strong rainbow beginning in his heart and then stretching out through the air to my heart. In this way we would stay connected to each other all night. I also would repeat a little poem which we made up, that went something like this:

I wrap you in a rainbow of light
To care for you all through the night.
Your guardian angel watches from above
And showers you with her great love.

Simon's frequent nightmares disappeared within three nights and have not returned. Though it is not a nightly ritual anymore, as the children are now much older, I still get the occasional request to 'please wrap me in a rainbow' after a tough day at school or when there's been some upset. There have been many times in my life when I would have loved someone to wrap *me* up in rainbow!

This ritual is particularly useful for the child who has a serious illness or whose parent has one. It is not just the child who benefits, we Mums enjoy it too. During my illness I was separated from my children for weeks at a time and each night I would always send them a rainbow, as they did to me. Some of this time I was in Europe and America whilst the children were in Australia with their father, and yet we knew these rainbows were always sent and delivered. Love can bridge all distances. Surely the substance of rainbows is love.

I know many children to whom sending rainbows continues to be very important. These children became accustomed to sending them to a parent when it was the parent who had the illness. It was the child's way of sending love and healing. Even after the parent has died, the ritual continues, the child knowing their rainbow is being received wherever their loved one is. For the child it is a sacred time of joining with someone they love who is no longer with them.

This technique allows us comfort and a tangible way of expressing our emotions. With a protracted illness, often it is not solutions we are needing. Sometimes it is just the strength to continue, day after day with seemingly no end in sight. And still the uncertainty of what the end will bring . . .

Some people mistakenly believe that to be positive is to only look on the outcome which they would like to see. So, to be positive is to have things one hundred per cent the way we would like them to be. This presupposes we know precisely what is the best outcome. One of my great realisations when I was sick was that, not only did I *not* know what was best for everyone else in the world (!) but I didn't have a clue what was best for me either. I genuinely believed if things were not the way *I* thought they were meant to be, then they had to be wrong. Such was my judgemental attitude at that time. This attitude precluded any self-acceptance. At this stage I had never heard of the concept of self-love or self-acceptance.

Many people regard thoughts or conversations about death and dying as being thoughts of 'negativity' or 'failure' or 'being morbid'. Death is not the opposite of life. Fear is the only thing which cuts us off from experiencing life abundantly. We live through the process of dying. Each and every one of us is going to pass through the experience of death, and to *not* talk about it can isolate the patient who, rest assured, is thinking about it at some level. Death is one of the most mysterious and awesome adventures upon which we are all obliged to embark, and to openly share with our loved ones the concepts, uncertainties and fears we hold can bring us to a much greater depth of intimacy and understanding. I have seen many families smiling through clenched teeth, putting every new lump down to a 'healing' of some kind. This increases the stress many-fold and can cause an unnecessary and painful wall of separation between loved ones. When these fears and uncertainties are acknowledged and, perhaps, tears are shed, we pick ourselves up again and once more are ready to overcome the obstacles that obstruct our way to experiencing peace. Sometimes we do not need to overcome, we can choose to walk around the obstacle. For instance, we cannot always overcome pain and yet we can develop techniques whereby it is more than tolerable.

One supporter had the realisation one day that it was O.K. not to cope. She had been a 'coper' all her life and found the situation of caring for her sick husband was sometimes overwhelming. She found it very liberating to give herself permission not to cope for the day! Personally, I am not fond of the word 'cope'. When we talk about someone who is coping quite well with a crisis, we usually mean that they are maintaining their composure on the outside regardless of how they are feeling on the inside. It is far healthier to express our feelings of inadequacy, frustration, fear or whatever. Once these feelings are expressed we are more able to continue with what is necessary in the situation.

A note about the telephone: its incessant ringing with people enquiring after the patient can be exhausting. Consider renting, or buying, or borrowing an answering machine. Then you can either leave a message saying when it is convenient for you to take calls or you can re-direct phone-calls to some other person who is willing to fulfil this function. Failing that, leave the phone off the hook. It *is* your home and you can choose when you wish to be available to people.

There is no easy solution to the problems faced by the support person. There will be days when nothing seems to go right and disappointments are in the air. Be gentle with yourself. Avoid having to 'cope'! With some thought and effort, create your *own* support system. The very best thing that you can bring to your loved one is peace of mind and a calm attitude. To achieve the qualities of serenity will certainly take an effort.

The following list provides possible ways of creating that support for yourself. Choose the things which seem to feel 'right' for you. They are not in any preferential order; some will feel right and others not. Good luck with your efforts!

1 Regular relaxation and recreation. We 're-create' ourselves

during meditation practices.

2 A good nourishing diet which provides all necessary nutrients for health.

3 Appropriate vitamin or mineral supplements if there is a deficiency.

4 A regular massage, perhaps with a therapist who will visit the home.

5 If it is your partner who is sick, arrange some time for just the two of you to be together.

6 Enlist the willing aid of neighbours and friends to do many of the mundane physical tasks.

7 Continue contact with supportive friends.

8 Despite the tiring onslaught of stress, retain your own self-image by having your hair done, attending your classes, or whatever.

9 See a funny movie whenever the opportunity presents itself!

10 Practise meditation — remember, that can be the glazed state that comes over ardent gardeners when watering their plants at sunset.

11 Take time alone for self-reflection.

12 It's O.K. not to cope. Be gentle with yourself on those uphill days.

13 Let go of maintaining the 'perfect image' of being a supporter.

14 Feel free to express your emotions. Remember tears are healing.

15 Don't hesitate to get professional counselling if there are difficulties in communication. If there were problems in the relationship before the illness, they probably haven't disappeared because of it.

16 If finances permit, arrange to have someone come to clean your home regularly, so your time can be better spent.

17 Above all, respect yourself and know you are doing your very best.

CHOICES

I want to say something here about choices for the patient, even though it may not seem to be relevant to caring for the carer. By giving the patient choices, we can certainly alleviate some of the stress on ourselves. Never is the offering of choices more important than when a person is ill and not able to control the major things in life. When we are sick and dependent on those around us for our physical care, it is much appreciated if we are given choices wherever possible. For instance,

'Would you prefer to have your bath before or after dinner?'
'Would you prefer to have a bath or a shower?'
'Would you like to have a walk before or after lunch?'
'Would you prefer your soup hot or cold?'

These may sound very simple little concessions to make and yet, remembering Vicki's story, we can see what a difference the small consideration of choices brings.

To serve others effectively, we must respect and care for ourselves. In this way we retain our own inner calm and strength and are thus able to give these qualities to others. It is these qualities which assist us in true healing. A frazzled partner is of limited assistance to someone who is unwell. A calm and positive carer can bring healing and wholeness to those they are with.

Chapter Seven

Visualisation Techniques

Our natural state is to be healthy, happy, fulfilled and, above all, able to extend and receive love — to feel confident and able to function in a completely satisfying manner. When this is not happening and these feelings are absent in our lives then, clearly, something has gone wrong. It becomes necessary for us to examine ourselves to find what we are holding back or holding on to that is causing our suffering.

As human beings we have a truly remarkable ability in that we can change whatever we hold in our minds. We can be the masters of our own minds by changing our thoughts. Thoughts are powerful, and we have thousands of them every day. Even though we think we are in control of our lives, we are plagued by the incessant activity of the mind. We can't remember a time in our lives when we didn't have thoughts. They drift through in a constant stream. We underestimate the power these thoughts have on our lives.

If we have programmed our mind with negative images and thoughts then the mind will accept those thoughts as being 'true'. With understanding and patience those thoughts and images can be altered and a more healthy way of looking at things developed.

The key to thought control is *habit.* Are you aware of the thoughts you most frequently hold? Do you habitually expect the best or the worst in any situation? Do you hold judgements or criticisms of your family, friends and associates — seeing them through an habitual 'veil' of judgement?

Begin to observe the thoughts which you hold in your mind. Sometimes you have to be very quick to catch them. The Indian teachers have long described the mind as 'a wild drunk monkey swinging through tree tops'. To tame the monkey and keep it on a leash can become our aim. Anyone who sets out to tame the mind will be rewarded.

Some people are 'worriers'. They weren't born that way, they gradually developed — probably through childhood or adolescence. If there isn't something going on in their lives to worry about they feel insecure, and will often create a worry, just so they can be comfortable with their usual thinking patterns.

Some people expect to be successful at whatever they attempt. And, not surprisingly, they are. The only thing the 'worriers' are usually successful at is — you guessed it — worrying!

There are others who always expect to fail. And they do. If you have an expectation of failure, then it is very likely that you won't put all your enthusiasm and effort into whatever project is at hand. It is a self-perpetuating mechanism that ensures your thinking is 'true'. This 'truth' you hold about yourself is not a fixed 'law' for you unless you choose to have it so. It is entirely up to you whether you are willing to make the effort to change. No-one else can do it for you. Only you can create the reality which you choose to experience.

Nature abhors a vacuum. So if we are unhappy about the way we feel and we choose to eliminate certain behaviour patterns that cause us distress, it is imperative that we have something strong and uplifting to put in the place of those thoughts which we choose to discard. We need to *want* to change our negative and constricting ideas to ones of positive receptivity, vitality, abundant health or whatever it is we desire.

Imagination is a powerful tool we can use for this purpose. It is not enough for us to say that we wish we weren't so negative about something. Often the negative programme by which we are living has been in our subconscious since infancy, so to eradicate such deeply held notions requires real dedication.

For many people, change is a frightening thing. The familiar is comfortable. Our negative thoughts are 'ours' and sometimes we will go to great lengths to protect them, even when they are damaging to us, or, at the very least, causing us stress. Sometimes we hold onto these old patterns of thinking because that was the way our mother or father always thought.

There is a lovely story that illustrates this. One day, a little girl was watching her mother preparing a leg of pork for baking. She asked her mother why she cut the bone off the end of the leg before she put it into the pan for baking. Her mother replied that that was the way she always did it because she had watched *her* mother do it. So they then went to Grandma and asked her why she always cut the end off the leg of pork before she cooked it. Grandma replied that *that* was the way *her* mother had always prepared the roast. Off they went to Great-grandma and asked her why she always cut the end off the leg of pork before she baked it. Great-grandma replied that the pan was too small and that was the only way the leg would fit!

Sometimes there is no good reason behind our actions. The thoughts which empower them are just habitual. Great-grandma had an excellent reason for cutting the end off the leg of pork. Likewise we can find an appropriate solution in one situation but then we go off and foist that same solution onto a totally different circumstance where it may be entirely inappropriate. Perhaps we were shut in our bedroom for an extended period of time as a young child, and, now in adulthood, we find enclosed spaces confining or stressful. Or, perhaps when we ate fish one time, a bone became stuck in our throat and frightened us. Perhaps we made that our last fish meal. Each one of us has our own collection of 'truths'. The situation which first prompted our 'truth' may no longer even be remembered but we live out our lives according to the decisions we made at that time.

These decisions can be far more crippling than the choice never to eat fish again. If we failed once we might have the subtle programming in our mind which says, 'I'll never make it' or, 'My life is a mess' or, simply, 'I'm a failure'. Other subtle negative programmes may chant into our minds thoughts like:

'No-one understands me'
'I'm so disappointed in myself'
'I wish I was someone else'
'I'm a loser'
'I can't finish anything'
'I'm worthless'
'I don't deserve love'

Perhaps sickness is the body's cry of distress over self-imposed emotional suffering? Visualisation techniques or guided imagery provide one of the most powerful tools for changing this negative programming. They use our imagination in a powerful way which can actually bring about physiological changes in our bodies. This approach is a means of communicating with the autonomic processes which occur without our conscious awareness. We have no consciousness of the functioning of our immune system, yet it is still busy about its work without our active participation.

Although you may be unaware of it, you are already familiar with the techniques of visualisation. Throughout your life, whenever the thought of an ice-cream, going for a swim, taking a shower, or any of the many activities of a lifetime comes into your mind, a brief picture of that event flashes through. You need to be quick sometimes to catch it, but sure enough it is there.

Some people are more visually oriented than others. Some spend hours fantasising or daydreaming; some claim it is better then the real thing! Spend a moment thinking about a holiday on a beautiful tropical island. Think of the golden sands, the vibrant colours in the waters surrounding this island, the vast blue dome of the sky above, the palms swaying in a soft, cooling breeze and so on. Probably, at the very least, you experienced flashes of colours, and isolated images even whilst just reading the words. Our more visual readers would perhaps have experienced much more. Some probably even smelt the sea air and felt the sand under their feet! There will be others who found that while reading even these few sentences they became slightly more relaxed.

Try another one. Let the image of a lemon, cut into quarters come into your mind. Now, in you mind's eye see yourself biting deep into one of the quarters. What happened? Did you produce a lot of saliva in your mouth? Here's another. A blackboard with a teacher standing beside it. She looks at you with a mischievous gleam in her eye as she scrapes her long fingernails down the board from top to bottom. What happened that time? This last example probably produced strongly felt but less tangible sensations in your body. An overall cringing perhaps?

These examples demonstrate the connection between your mind and your body. When we hold positive, healing thoughts in our mind every cell 'feels' the confidence and caring that such thoughts bring. We can send soothing and comforting thoughts out to areas of our body in need of them by holding in our mind some suitable image that is calming, and letting the effects of that image flow out. So also, we can create a dynamic and vibrant feeling throughout our body by holding a more powerful image. The development of skills in this area is a major strength in our ability to heal ourselves.

We have a tendency in our society to look for and believe the 'bad' news rather than the 'good'. When we visit the doctor, we put on our super-sensitive ears so we don't miss a thing he says. We strain to hear the intonation, the emphasis, the choice of words. Usually by the time we leave, we can't remember much of what he *did* say, and yet we will certainly remember any 'negative' intonation. Some doctors will still talk about a 'time limit' for their patients. To be told we 'won't see Christmas' or that we've 'got three to six months' is a great shock to our whole being. A doctor can still explain to us that we are very ill — without giving a specific time-frame. And we *all* benefit by hearing about the exceptions to such prognoses. We need to move away from statistical thinking and be more concerned with the individual — ourself. Every doctor knows of the exceptional patient who didn't fall into the statistical framework he or she was 'meant to'. It requires a lot of courage to put aside the medical predictions and put all efforts into living. I believe sometimes the doctor's words cut so deeply into an individual that they are unable to muster any positivity within themselves. All hopes are dashed. The truth is there is *always* hope, no matter what the statistics say.

One of my patients, a man with AIDS, was told he wouldn't see Christmas a couple of years ago. He had been working very diligently with his juices, visualisation, diet, exercise, vitamins and so on, and was feeling really well. His T-cells were increasing and the Kaposi's sarcoma lesions (a kind of cancer) were fading from visible detection. However, his doctor told him not to get his hopes up because he would still definitely be dead by Christmas! It is no skin off anyone's nose to say instead, 'You seem to be feeling much better than when I saw you last. Your lesions are going, your T-cells are increasing. Whatever you are doing to help yourself, keep it up!' That's a win/win situation. Everyone feels encouraged. Surely the doctor feels encouraged to see someone making the most of his situation and apparently being rewarded for his efforts? Even if the patient does die by Christmas, he feels that his doctor has been as caring and encouraging of his efforts as possible. As it is, this particular man has had AIDS for more than 3 years now, walks 5 km each day, plays squash or tennis 3 times a week and enjoys his organic garden and cooking from home-grown produce. He says his quality of life has never been so good.

The reason I have spent quite a time on the effect of the diagnosis is because most of us will believe what we are told, especially when told by a 'specialist'. It is difficult to conjure up a picture of hope when all the news seems to be depressing. The mind seems to be numbed. It takes a real effort to evoke in the mind an image of ourselves as whole and healthy. And yet, it can be done!

One man, very ill with cancer, incorporated into his visualisation the picture of himself escorting his daughter down the aisle at her wedding. At the time she was only a child of 8. It gave him great comfort and inspired his positive efforts to get well.

We need to dream courageously. No great achievement is accomplished without a great dream preceding it. Give yourself permission to dream about a glorious future. Allow all the trimmings to be present in your dreaming. Be specific about what it is that you wish to acquire and then have the courage to focus on it as if it were already on its way to you.

One man, Brian, who had AIDS decided after his diagnosis that there was no way he was going to die before he learned to ride a horse — a life-long dream. He was very thin and suffered with chronic and uncontrollable diarrhoea. He took himself off to a riding establishment, and away he went. He took lessons to perfect his technique and, in time, decided he wanted to particpate in the 'hunts'. This involved jumps, long hours in the saddle and very impressive apparel. To see him proudly sitting on his horse was a joy indeed. To overcome the problems he had with diarrhoea, he would eat constipating food for two days before a hunt, wear double-panty nappies designed for babies and he was set. His tremendous spirit was an inspiration to all who knew him. He would say, 'I can see myself now, sailing over the jumps with ease.'

If, in our mind's eye, we are projecting positive, vibrant images then they become our expectation of the future. Some may say that it is not being realistic to project a positive image when we have been told we are dying. Surely what matters is how we live every moment. People sometimes forget that even though we may have a shortened life-span, right now we are living — not dying. Who wants to make a full-time occupation out of dying? This is often brought home to me when I see a self-sown plant growing in a most precarious position, perhaps out of a crack in the road, or out of a tiny space between the bricks on a stairwell. The plant didn't think, 'This isn't a good place to grow, I might get trodden on or run over by a truck. There's no-one to water me and there's next to no soil. Not a good idea at all.'

The plant just lives. It has an inbuilt urge to survive. So do we. Whilst there is life, live it. Not just by existing but by giving it every affirmation possible.

To be surrounded by beauty uplifts the spirit. A bowl of flowers, a sunset, a child's smile, leaves in the sunshine — all these things act as powerful and uplifting images.

We need to be diligent in watching the images which come into our mind. It is useful to have a powerful and positive image to place there whenever we detect a depressing or pessimistic attitude arising.

A very practical way of strengthening this exercise practice is to spend several sessions each day implanting these images into the mind. Firstly, you must find an image which seems appropriate to you. Many people don't really know what they want. They only know what they *don't* want. They know they don't want to die, for instance. And yet, they have no clear image in their minds of how they really want to live. For many people life just happens to them. We experience a richness in our lives when we actually have a goal to aim for and then work towards it, like Brian. His goal was to learn to ride a horse, then to go on a hunt. He set about bringing those images to life. He didn't wait to see if a horse just happened by. In fact, he went to great lengths to ensure the success of his goal.

In these more 'formalised' sessions we sit down and focus on the images we have selected. We project them powerfully onto the screen of our mind. Tune out any other thoughts or impressions and let your mind be completely full of the image. Allow the feelings belonging with that image to surface and let yourself indulge in those feelings. Let them come alive in you now as if that *is* your present reality. Trust the image you have projected is already on its way to you in its fullness and you can, even now, feel its effect.

When I was unwell I worked with two images in particular. The first one came about naturally as I would sit in the early morning sun. I would let my body relax and then concentrate on feeling the sunshine on my skin. After a while I would begin to breathe in the sunshine. I would visualise its warmth as a soft golden cloud of light gently filling my chest. I could feel it flowing down into my tummy and abdomen, down into the hips and buttocks, down through the thighs, into the knees, calves and into my feet and toes. A soft billowy cloud of golden light. Down through my arms into the elbows and forearms, wrists, hands and fingertips. Finally I would fill my throat, neck and the inside of my head with the golden glow of the sun. I would concentrate all my thoughts and attention on breathing in this golden sparkling light, until every cell felt like it was surrounded in a halo of light. After some minutes concentrating on filling my body with light I would visualise the borders of my body dissolving so that the sunshine outside, and the sunshine inside, became one light. I became the sun. I would then experience being the sun for however long it felt wonderful. It usually extended for at least half an hour, oftentimes much longer.

This is a lovely image to work with and quite simple. We are all familiar with the gentle touch of the sunshine on our skin. It is an easy step to visualise it as light and draw it into our bodies. It only takes concentration. It leads easily into the meditation aspect where one just experiences a feeling of 'being'.

The other visualisation which I developed was more concentrated and active in its implementation. Again, I would begin with a relaxation, letting the body soften and open. Then I would begin to breathe in angels. I'd always been rather partial to angels and they seemed to be an image I felt comfortable with. My little angels were exquisitely beautiful, each one different from the other. I don't know how many there were but I used to breathe them in and then place them every three inches around my body. I always started at my right thumb and put an angel just inside the tip of my thumb, the next one at the base, index finger tip, base of finger and so on — right throughout my body. When I could 'see' and feel every angel in place, all at the same time, I would get them to start sounding the word 'Om' to each other. This is an ancient Sanskrit mantra, rather like our 'Amen'. I had been studying Sanskrit for some years and the way in which I had learned the fundamentals of Sanskrit was by sounding the very simplest of its components. It had always been an incredibly powerful exercise and was very effective in stilling the mind. So, choosing the sound of 'Om' was, again, entirely born out of my previous experience.

When the angels sang this sound to each other, I would experience it both as a feeling as well as 'seeing' or imaging the sound as a vibration travelling through the bloodstream, through the muscles, tendons and ligaments. I would see it flow right through the bones into the bone marrow. And I would feel the power of that sound setting all the cells dancing to that vibration. As the vibration from one angel met up with the vibration from the next, a network would be formed throughout the body. This network became more and more complex until every cell in the body was 'touched' by it, and then it would dissolve into the overall experience of that sound and feeling. If thoughts or distractions entered the mind I had a little volume-control down on the left hand corner of the screen in my mind and I would simply turn up the volume until no other experience was possible. In this way, I dealt with the pain I experienced. It also shifted my perception of my situation from one of despair to something quite different.

As can be seen from both of these peaceful visualisations, my preference is to work with images which have a sense of increasing a positive experience within the body. Other people may find it more positive to work with a more aggressive approach to their disease.

One man, Bob, who had AIDS, visualised his T-cells as pac men with big feet, smiles on their faces, wearing T-shirts with a capital 'T' on the front to denote their function in his body. He would visualise these little T-cell pac men pouring out of his thymus gland into his bloodstream. Whenever they came across the unwanted virus, these little pac men would jump up and down on them until they were dead. Then he would see them removed from his body through the bloodstream and then out through the bowel. He did this many times a day.

The most important thing to remember when working out an appropriate visualisation for your own situation is to choose something which comes easily from your own background or experience.

Another man in his mid-forties, had lung cancer. He would visualise his chemotherapy as weedkiller which was only effective on his cancer cells and left his other tissues entirely intact. After he had visualised the weedkiller doing its job, he would 'see' his immune system mulching the areas which had previously harboured the weeds. He would finish his visualisation by planting into the mulch an array of his favourite flowers. Many people have difficulty in accepting chemotherapy as a positive help to themselves. Oftentimes it is looked upon as a necessary evil. It is really important to rectify this attitude. If you experience the chemotherapy as a toxic, poisonous substance flowing into your body, it is very likely to cause you more side-effects than if you believe this substance is liquid gold pouring its healing power into your body. We *do* have the power to choose what we will hold in our minds. If we have chosen to have chemotherapy then we should follow that choice up with positive feelings and images about what the outcome of the treatment will be. The same principle applies to radiotherapy. Those rays can be powerful forces of destruction or they can be powerful shining images of healing light.

Janine, a young woman with breast and lung cancer, was undergoing a series of radiotherapy treatments to her chest area. She had been warned that her oesophagus would also be damaged and would be quite painful in the weeks to come. Janine decided that at each treatment she would place around her oesophagus a cloud of cooling blue light which would protect that area from any damage. She firmly believes that because of her imaging, she never experienced any feelings of discomfort from the treatments. Another woman, in her early thirties, would visualise all her healthy cells 'standing back' to let the rays pass through so that they only destroyed the cancerous cells.

Drawing can be very useful in helping to clarify how we really feel about our disease and its treatment. Sometimes we can *think* we are very positive, and yet when we draw our disease or our chemotherapy, another image may well emerge. Our subconscious attitudes and feelings are easily visible through our drawings. I often ask people to draw their disease. On another sheet of paper, I ask them to draw their treatment. These drawings can then be discussed and the fears or anxieties evident in the drawings can be aired.

Jenny is in her forties and felt very trapped by her unhappy homelife. She felt overwhelmed by her powerlessness to change her home environment. When she was diagnosed with a tumour around her gall-bladder, she felt even more overwhelmed. However, her family expected her to 'be positive' and that she could take all this in her stride. This was largely their defence against having to support her emotionally. On the outside she appeared to be quite positive and yet her drawings belied this perception. She had drawn her gall-bladder as a very weak and ill-defined organ. Wrapped around the organ was a large black spider with a rather crooked smile upon its face. Not a happy smile. More of a mean and conquering one. The picture she drew of her treatment showed a further assault being made upon her. She had drawn her radiotherapy as black arrows penetrating her body. Once these drawings were discussed, Jenny's feelings flooded to the surface. Her long-held back tears flowed freely as she recounted her years of unhappiness within her marriage. She felt that her cancer was just one more thing she had to deal with in her unsupportive environment, and the smile upon the spider's face was the final insult.

It took a lot of effort on Jenny's part to begin to restore her feelings of self-respect and worthiness. It took courage to actively seek counselling at a time when she was undergoing fairly gruelling treatments. Yet, she did. In time, her whole family underwent counselling and the relationships at home between her husband and herself and her grown sons began to improve. As the months passed, her drawings began to include more light and the images of her gall-bladder became more robust. The spider was replaced by shadows. Shadows are dispelled by light. This showed she felt she had a greater sense of control. This very much reflected her progress as the tumour became smaller.

It might seem that it is necessary to be at least a rudimentary artist to work with drawings. This couldn't be further from the truth. All that is necessary is a willingness to explore. The people in the picture can be very simply drawn. It is best not to make them stick figures, but that is the only requirement. It is preferable to work with white paper and coloured pencils or crayons. Felt tip pens are not really suitable as no gradation is possible in shading.

Some people have difficulty in actually 'seeing' any images at all when they attempt to visualise. Drawing the visualisation can oftentimes be helpful in focusing the mind upon the chosen image.

Another suggestion for those who find it difficult to visualise an image in their mind's eye is to work just with light or colour. If you are using a tape which embodies a visualisation, then perhaps just go with the sound of the voice or music or the atmosphere of what is being said, rather than judging yourself harshly for not being able to 'see' what is being talked about. Self-judgement or criticism is the antithesis of what the visualisation is designed for so avoid the temptation. For most people it only requires consistent practice before the images begin to flow easily.

The following visualisation technique is the one I spoke of earlier, where we can work with sunshine or light. It is a very simple and easily learnt technique. Like meditation, although the skill is simply learnt it does take consistent practice to achieve all of its benefits. Let a friend read, very slowly, the following technique out loud to you, or read it yourself onto a tape and play it back frequently until you are adept at the technique. Alternatively, an explanation of visualisation and this technique are available on cassette. This cassette is available from the address at the end of the book.

To be read, very slowly:

Allow your eyes to close over lightly. Let your body settle into a position in which you feel comfortable. If you are sitting, allow your spine to be as comfortably erect as possible. Begin by taking some long, slow, soft breaths. Feel yourself settling in to your body. Breathing out all tension, all mental activity quietening down. Just long, slow, soft breaths that let you relax deeply.

As you breathe in this way, feel your body beginning to soften. Letting go of all rigidity. Your body open and soft and flexible. Let your feet soften and become warm. Bringing your attention to the soft warmth in your feet. Each toe full of softness. The muscles within your feet relaxing, loosening.

The ankles softening. Let them be loose. The muscles of the calves, relaxing and softening. Let your knees be loose. Let your thighs soften and spread against the chair or mattress. Feel the texture of your clothing against the skin of your thighs. Even the bones seeming to soften. Let your buttocks cushion and support you without any tension. Feel them spread against the chair or mattress.

Let your abdomen gently rise and fall with each breath at your own rhythm. Deep within your abdomen, allow each of the organs to soften. Their borders smoothing out, relaxing deeply. Allow the warmth and comfort within the abdomen to flow deep within the pelvis.

Feel it spreading gently up into the tummy and solar plexus. If there is any tightness in the solar plexus, just above your navel, then breathe into that area and allow it to soften and open.

Warmth and relaxation flowing on into the chest. Notice the movements of your chest as you breathe. The way your clothes move against the skin as you breathe.

Focus on your heart and allow it to soften and open. Relax your shoulders. Feel all the tension draining out of your shoulders. Feel ripples of relaxation flowing down and across your back. Over your shoulder blades, over your waist. Let that relaxation flow down through your arms, into the elbows and forearms. Let the muscles drift away from the bones. Dissolving into stillness. Your wrists soft, yielding. The muscles, tendons and ligaments within your hands softening, becoming like loose elastic. Right down into your fingertips, letting go.
Muscles softening throughout the whole body. Each breath

drawing in deeper relaxation.

Allow your throat to be open and relaxed and let go of all unnecessary tension in your neck. If you are sitting, let your head float very lightly at the top of your spine. As it floats, feel your spine lengthening and stretching, lifting your diaphragm.

Let your lower jaw drop just enough to let your teeth part. Allow your tongue to soften in your mouth. Soften the lips and cheeks. All the muscles around the eyes, softening and spreading as your relaxation deepens. Let the space between your eyebrows widen as your forehead relaxes. Soft temples, ears and scalp.

The whole of your body relaxing more deeply with each breath. Breathing in peace and calm. Feel all tension in body and mind draining out with each outward breath. Gently in. Gently out. Each breath takes you deeper into relaxation.

Now imagine a light just above your head. You may see it as a brilliant ball of light. Or perhaps you can see a radiant sun. See its golden healing light radiating out from its centre. You may begin to feel the warmth of that light gently showering down onto the top of your head. A soft golden light, full of warmth and healing.

Let that light gently penetrate through the top of your head, until the whole of the inside of your head is filled with a soft golden glowing light. Behind your eyes, through all the muscles of your face, a soft glowing golden light. Filling your mouth, cradling your tongue in soft light.

Feel the light slowly moving down through your throat and neck. Filling them with soft sparkling light. Dissolving all tension. And on into your shoulders. Light pouring from its unending source. A soft healing golden light soothing all the cells as it flows down and across your back. Flowing over and through the shoulder blades. On over the waist. Soothing, healing light.

Let it flow into the cavity of your chest filling it with a sparkling cloud of golden light. Every cell healed, comforted, soothed by the presence of this sparkling light. The heart cradled in light.

Feel the healing presence of this golden light flowing freely down through the arms. Bringing rest and peace and light. You may find that your fingers begin to tingle or pulsate with the presence of this golden, healing energy. Let the light flow right on out through the fingertips. Flowing from its unending source. Light and peace filling the body.

Soft billowy clouds of light flowing down through the tummy. Softening and soothing. Each cell surrounded and healed by the presence of light. Tiny little sparkles of golden light flooding into the abdomen. Filling the abdomen with light and peace.

Each inward breath drawing more of this healing light into the body. The pelvis cradled in a golden radiance.

Soft sparkling light filling the buttocks and hips. Feel it flowing down through the thighs. The bones melting into light and peace. The knees softening, dissolving into light. The lower legs filled with golden clouds of light. Flowing right into the feet. The toes filling with light, dissolving into light. The light flowing on out through the end of the toes. An unending source of light pouring through the body.

Let the tissues, the muscles, dissolve into the golden, healing light. The borders of your organs melting away. Soothed and comforted by the soft presence of light. Feel the warmth throughout your body. Each breath drawing more light, more healing in to your body.

The heart melting away into light. All tension softening, dissolving into light.

Bones softening, dissolving into light.

Floating in an ocean of light. A vast ocean, without limit or border. Only light, only peace. Floating in this ocean of peace and light. Effortlessly drifting through light.

Now, with each inward breath, draw in light. With each outward breath let the borders of your body dissolve. Melting into that ocean of light. Becoming the ocean of light without border or limit. At one with the ocean of light. Each outward breath dissolving more into light. Only light, only peace. An ocean of light and peace.

Thoughts, feelings, drifting in this vast ocean of light and peace. Sensations floating in awareness. Each thought, each feeling, each sensation melting back into the ocean. Each sound melting back into the vast awareness. Without border or limit. Only light and peace.

(long pause)

Gently begin to bring your awareness back into your body. Begin to take some long, soft, deeper breaths. Breathing in light and energy. Feel the tone beginning to return to your body as your awareness comes fully back into your body. The muscle tone returning to arms and legs.

Begin moving your hands and feet just a little. Staying with the peace, bringing it back with you.

Begin to stretch the rest of your body. Enjoying the refreshment, the relaxation in all the muscles of your body.

Taking your time to bring all of your awareness back into your body. Enjoy the peace and calm within your body.

In your own time, just as you're ready, allow the eyes to open. You may wish to close them for a little longer and open them in your own time.

Another really powerful visualisation which I developed during my illness was one in which I worked with the image of Christ. In the very darkest days of my illness I experienced an awful despair and hopelessness. So bad did it become, I took to praying at night *not* to wake in the morning. I loathed getting weaker and my preference was to die immediately, without the languishing bit.

However, each morning, there I'd be again. Realising these were not very healing prayers, I decided to change my tactics.

As soon as I woke up in the morning, I would visualise Christ sitting on the end of my bed. I figured Christ knew more about healing than any other Being. He was not alone in my room. I also invited His mother Mary, St Francis, Sai Baba, Yogananda and any angels who might be available. I would then reflect on the qualities which I perceived in Christ. He never gave up, He stuck it out to the end. His peace. His serenity. His compassion. His love. Then I would see these qualities radiating out from His body as light. And I would begin to breathe in that Light, breathing in His qualities. Seeing them as Light which flowed down into my feet, my legs, my abdomen and so on, right through my body. Until the whole of my body was full of His Light. His peace. His joy. His serenity. His compassion and love. His patience and perseverence.

By the time I had practised this technique for a few minutes, all thoughts and feelings of despair, isolation, fear and hopelessness had vanished. I only experienced His qualities.

At the end of this exercise, I would visualise Christ becoming smaller and smaller until He was just the right size to place into my heart and I would put Him there. And, again, I would see Him radiating His qualities throughout my body, throughout my mind. In this way we kept company.

It does not matter if this entire exercise is in my imagination. It is a matter of choice. I can choose to be miserable, hopeless and full of despair or I can choose to experience light and peace. Frankly, I prefer the latter. One frame of mind is dark and inward, rather like a black hole; the other is light and expansive.

To have this latter attitude is also much nicer for our carers. There's nothing more depressing than caring for a 'black hole'. I firmly believe also that the attitude we hold will directly influence the healing process within our bodies. A depressed and hopeless mind will influence our immune system along with every organic particle of our bodies.

To experience deep peace and love in our lives is healing. When minds and spirits are healed we are creating the very best environment for physical healing. It is up to us how we are going to create peace in our lives. The peace is always there and yet we need to make a conscious decision for peace.

For those who have no spiritual beliefs, peace can still be a reality. For example, to visualise a beautiful flower in all its glory . . . Then to breathe in its beauty, its colour and fragrance. To breathe in the very essence of the mystery of the flower. To visualise its qualities flowing in to your body as light, flowing down into your feet and so on, just like the exercise with Christ, will bring a profound sense of peace and serenity.

For those who have definite spiritual beliefs, call on them and give them new power to heal and establish peace in your lives. I have been greatly helped by many religions and I believe every one at its roots has been inspired by God.

The Christ-visualisation mentioned before is a very powerful means by which we can change our consciousness, and I use it often in my practice with people who have a relationship with Christ.

In the groups where I teach visualisation techniques I usually structure the visualisation around familiar natural images. Perhaps working with the image of a garden, with a beautiful waterfall and pool in it. Or working with the sunshine, letting its light radiate down onto our bodies, filling them with its light. Or with the rainforest, or an ocean or river. People's experiences with these images are often profoundly moving, and they will describe what they have experienced in very 'spiritual' terms. When the heart is touched, the mind is bypassed. Many of our religious beliefs are things of the mind. Our experience of God, or of a Higher Source is always heart-felt. The mind may get busy with the experience afterwards to try to make sense of it, or to fit it into a neat pigeon-hole. The greatest struggle in life with each human being is the war between the heart and the mind. The heart 'knows' something and yet the mind replies that it cannot understand this 'something' which the heart 'knows' and therefore does not believe in it.

The mind is forever questioning and is often satisfied with superficial answers. When your heart asks 'Why?' it wants only the Truth.

Chapter Eight

Meditation — a Key to Life

Meditation is indeed one of the golden keys to life. More than any other technique it opens up new vistas of experience and enrichment, awareness and joy. It is simple to practise and its benefits are readily available, even to the novice.

Meditation is the state of being with one's self, right now. It has no particular religious connection though it may be a profoundly moving and even spiritual experience. It depends on what *you* denote as spiritual.

Meditation is simple to learn and with regular practice brings many benefits. These may range from greater peace of mind, to a relaxed body. Meditation also releases energy within the body which can be used for healing. Remember that a good day's worry is far more exhausting than a good day with an axe. After a day with the axe we fall into bed exhausted and sleep contentedly. After a day of worry we stumble off to bed and twitch all night.

When your mind is anxious or stressed your body secretes many chemicals and hormones into the bloodstream which inhibit the natural functions of your body, decreasing the activities of some whilst increasing the activities of others. Stress of itself is not a negative thing. It is essential to have stress in our lives. Stress provides us with challenge. Even gravity is a stress. By overcoming challenging stresses in our lives we gain satisfaction and fulfilment. However, stress over which we feel that we have no control can be very detrimental to our peace of mind and our health. Many people will be able to identify some severe stress in the previous six months to two years before they manifested any symptoms of their present disease. This time-frame is not arbitrary. Sometimes the stress goes back much further than that and it has been a gradual accumulation to the point where the body's defences can no longer cope, whilst for others there was one particular event or series of events which preceded the illness.

When we have a programme worked out for our healing, meditation gives us the impetus to keep on going. It affirms our own inner healing power and it activates the wisdom of healing within our body. When you cut yourself, your body quite naturally sets all the necessary processes in action to enable healing to take place. You don't need to panic and think, 'Oh my goodness, I had better send down some fibrin and a bit of collagen. Don't forget the leukacytes in case there are any bacteria!' It all just happens perfectly naturally. Your body has a perfect wisdom within it that knows precisely what is necessary for your health and well-being. All you need to do is to provide the ideal healing environment and, for the rest, trust that healing is taking place.

More than anything else you can do, meditation will give you all the fine energy you need to heal. Remember, your mind is not separate from your body, your emotions are not separate from your body. As human beings each of us is an integrated whole. The thoughts which we hold in our minds affect the functioning of our bodies. The feelings that we have, whether acknowledged or ignored, have an effect on our bodies. They are *our* experience of reality and therefore are real for us. Each person's reality is their own. The mind has an extraordinary capacity in which it can change the thoughts which it holds dear. This gives us a tremendous point of power in that we can change the thoughts which may cause us stress into those which lay down the foundations for greater peace, fulfilment and joy in our lives. This choice is unique to humankind.

One of the most powerful tools for change is the technique of meditation. Actually there are many techniques of meditation. The best technique is the one that works for you. There is no right technique, no higher or lower technique — nor is there one teacher. There are as many techniques as there are people. Allow yourself the freedom to find a right technique and a right teacher that works for you. In meditation the physiological responses to stress have an opportunity to re-establish the body's own equilibrium once more. You will notice that your breathing begins to slow down, the heart-rate and blood pressure drop. Your muscles relax and physiologically we come to rest as the mind begins to settle and a sense of ease and peace is experienced.

Meditation is like relaxation for the mind. It is very simple. Just as we bring our awareness to the various muscles in our body and allow them to soften and relax, so we observe the thoughts and feelings which pass through our mind. Observe and let go. Not holding onto thoughts, not adding to them. Just observe and let go. Meditation is a little like sitting deep below the ocean, at rest on the ocean floor. The thoughts are like waves up on the surface. They don't disturb our peace. If you find that you have started to be busy with the thoughts, just let them go again. Do the same with feelings which may arise. Not judging, not criticising yourself for having them. Let them come, and pass. Observe and let go. An ocean of awareness, not focusing on any particular thought or feeling. Be patient with yourself throughout your practice sessions. Treat meditation like a new adventure into unexplored territory. A journey within yourself.

There is nothing mysterious attached to learning the technique of meditation. The meditation technique at the end of this chapter is one that I have used for myself and for many others. You may wish to have a friend read it to you slowly or you may wish to make a tape of it so that you can play it back to yourself until you are quite familiar with the technique. Alternatively, I have put this technique down onto a cassette and details for ordering are at the back of this book. The benefit of having someone talk you through the process (as in a cassette tape) is that you are committed for a certain period of time. What often happens when we sit down to meditate, unless our self-discipline is really strong, is that 10 minutes or so into the practice we have thoughts like, 'Hmm, if I put the potatoes in the oven now, they would be ready when I finish meditating. Hmmm, while I'm up, I'll just put the hose on the petunias . . .' and before you know it, we're up and off and we never quite find the time to get back to our meditation.

I suggest that you practise these techniques regularly, preferably twice a day as a minimum. You will need to find out what the ideal length of time is for you. Also how frequently you need to meditate in order to feel a real benefit. Some people gain all their benefits in the first 10–15 minutes and for them to do a little, and often, may be best. Avoid falling into the trap of believing that meditation is difficult or requires long practice to become effective. It is actually very simple. Quite quickly you will begin to experience the benefits of meditation. Allow your own pattern of meditation to emerge. I find that most people can easily start off with two 40-minute sessions of relaxation and meditation per day. After awhile it becomes so inviting and enjoyable that you may find that you need to re-arrange your schedule so that you can do longer sessions.

Some of the benefits you will notice include a certain calmness in your attitude, and the things which used to distress you will become inconsequential. Your memory will improve and so will your powers of concentration. You will also find that you are able to accomplish more in your day, you will have more energy, and you may find you need less sleep. The sleep that you do have may be deeper and more refreshing.

It is a good idea to establish a place of meditation in your home. A room set aside for the purpose is great, and yet a corner of a room is ample also. Wear loose and comfortable clothing that does not restrict your breathing in any way. You may wish to make this corner or room special by placing an uplifting picture of Nature, or some fresh flowers there. For those who have any spiritual or religious leanings, an appropriate picture or symbol may help to instil a calm and reverential attitude. For some a cross or rosary is appropriate. You may find you are more comfortable in an upright chair which supports your head. Feel free to supplement your sitting position with cushions.

After a time you will find you begin to relax and become calm as soon as you enter that quiet and 'special' place. If you share your home with someone else you may wish to ask for their co-operation at the times when you choose to meditate. Or you could encourage them to join with you in your practice. It doesn't matter that there are sounds around you, though it is preferable to practise in a quiet environment. You may wish to leave a note on the door asking not to be disturbed, and take the telephone off the hook. Why not let your friends know that you practise meditation at certain times each day? Tell them that you consider it to be really important in assisting you in your recovery and ask for their co-operation in not visiting or telephoning you at those times. If you do need to break your meditation, it is not a problem. Just take a couple of long deep breaths, open your eyes and attend to whatever you need to, knowing that you will easily resume the depth of meditation when you return.

You may wonder how you will know *if* you are meditating. The hallmarks of meditation are that the mind becomes much quieter than usual and that your breathing is very light. If that is happening, trust that you are meditating. You will find it helpful to begin your sessions with some deep breathing. Begin with some long slow deep breaths to release any tension and to bring about a sense of calm and stillness. If you have any difficulty with breathing, work comfortably within your particular limitations. There may be the occasional person who finds, when concentrating on their breathing, that they begin to cough. For these folk, it is best to focus their attention on the rising and falling of the abdomen, or right at the entrance of their nostrils.

It is preferable to learn these techniques sitting comfortably upright in a chair or on the floor. There is a tendency, when lying down, to fall asleep. This sleep is usually very deep and refreshing, however, what we are endeavouring to learn is how to be fully conscious and yet deeply relaxed. Settle comfortably into your chair and allow your feet to rest flat upon the floor. You may wish to remove your shoes. Allow your spine to be as comfortably erect as possible so that you are not slouched down into the chair. Loosen your belt or any tight or restrictive clothing. Let your hands rest comfortably in your lap in a position where they won't slide off and distract you.

If you know that you have a problem in your body which will make it too difficult for you to remain in that position for about half an hour, then lie down with just a small pillow under your head for support. During your practice, if you need to scratch, cough, stretch or shift position, then do so and return to your practice. Don't turn your practice into a battle! Meditate just as long as you enjoy it and gently begin to stretch the boundaries. There is no more worthwhile or rewarding adventure than to discover who you are. Allow yourself the pleasure of the experience.

The following technique is the one which I have used with

many people to learn the simple skills of meditation. Although the skill is simply learnt it does take consistent practice to achieve all of its benefits. Remember, it may be read very slowly by a friend, or put on to a cassette tape or it is available by writing to the address in the back of the book:

Find a position that is comfortable for you, preferably sitting or lying down. Begin by taking some long slow deep breaths. Breathing in relaxation, breathing out all tension in your body and in your mind. Soft open, deep breaths that help you settle in to your body.

Set aside all the roles that you normally play amongst your family and friends, your work. Devote this next little while just to yourself. Really being with yourself. To create an environment for peace. And allow your breathing to return to its own natural rhythm.

Bring your awareness to your feet. To the soles of your feet. Feeling the sensations which arise. Where there is pressure, where there is space. And to the tops of your feet. The touch of air. The texture or pressure of anything touching the skin on the tops of your feet.

Then bring your awareness to your toes. Beginning with the big toes. And to the next. And next and so on down to the little toes. Letting the muscles soften and relax. Take your mind deep within your feet. To all the muscles, tendons and ligaments. Each strand of muscle softening. Becoming warm and comfortable. Allow your ankles to be loose. And the muscles of your calves to soften. Just hanging from the bones. Let your knees be relaxed. And the muscles of your thighs, let them soften and spread. Even the bones seeming to soften.

Feel the chair or the floor against the backs of your legs. The touch of your clothing against your thighs.

Relaxing your buttocks. Just let them spread. Cushioning and supporting you without any tension.

Let your abdomen gently rise and fall at your own rhythm. Take your awareness deep within your abdomen. Let each organ float in its own soft warm space.

Let that warmth flow deep within your pelvis. Let it spread up into your solar plexus and tummy. If you notice any tightness in your solar plexus, visualise it as a pond and see a pebble dropped right into its centre. And see those ripples of relaxation flowing out from its centre, softening and soothing.

And on into your chest. Feel each small movement as your ribcage expands and contracts with each breath. Let the air do the breathing for you. Allow your heart to be open and warm and soft.

Let go of all unnecessary tension in your shoulders. You may want to visualise two gentle hands resting on your shoulders that absorb any tension that is there and that send waves of relaxation down and across your back. Down through your upper arms into the elbows and forearms.

Let your arms rest quietly in your lap. You may find that they become very heavy or very light as you relax even deeper. Whichever feels right for you. Let your wrists be relaxed. And your hands at rest.

Each of the muscles softening, releasing all tension. Right down into your fingertips. You may find that they begin to pulsate or tingle with the soft presence of relaxation.

Allow your throat to be open and relaxed. Letting go of all unnecessary tension in your neck. If you are sitting you may like to visualise your head floating like a balloon at the top of a string, like your spine. Letting it float up toward the ceiling till it finds its own perfect balance.

Let your lower jaw drop just a little. Enough to let your teeth part. Allow your tongue to be soft in your mouth. Soft lips. Cheeks. All the little muscles around your eyes smoothing out and softening. Smoothing away all tension. And deep behind your eyes, let go of any straining, any trying to see. Allow the space between your eyebrows to widen as your forehead relaxes. Your temples and ears. The whole of your scalp. So that the whole of your body becomes deeply calm and relaxed. Every breath that you take helps you to relax even deeper. Any sounds that are around you are familiar and there is no need to judge or criticise or even to label the sounds. Let the sounds share each moment with you. A soft openness.

Now bring your awareness back to the toes, the feet and ankles. Allow the feet to fill with a soft silence. Filling silently with space. Breathing in space. The stillness expanding.

Flowing softly up through the calves of the legs. The knees filling with stillness. The thighs. Soaking in spaciousness. Softness. Let that silence flow into the hips and buttocks. A deep silence. A spaciousness. Soft openness. The abdomen filling with space and silence. Each organ resting in great quietness. Feel it spreading into the solar plexus. The stomach softly opening to stillness. Each breath bringing stillness into the body. As if the air breathes for you. The lungs full of a vast silence. The heart resting soft, cradled in peace. The spine dissolving into stillness. No holding. Only peace. Space.

Shoulders filled with soft openness. Let that softness flow down through the arms into the hands and fingers. Filling with a soft awareness. A vast stillness. Silence filling the body. The mind full of ease and peace.

Allow the throat to fill with space. The neck relaxing into stillness. Sensations floating through stillness. Each sensation coming, to pass. The jaw softening and opening. The muscles of the face slowly dissolving into great stillness. Behind the face. Letting go into silence. Soft openness. The body melting into silence. Dissolving into spaciousness. Boundaries dissolving. No resistance.

Mind and thought melting into peace. Mind and body, floating in peace and stillness. Each cell, cradled in warmth and peace. The awareness floating free in this great stillness. Softly opening to each unfolding moment. Resting gently in this vast silence.

Surrender into soft silence. No holding. No resistance. Letting go of the particular. Each thought dissolving into spaciousness. Soft silence.

(pause)

Become aware of your breathing again. Allow it to deepen. Each breath drawing energy into your body. Bring your awareness back in to your body. Feel the muscle-tone returning in to your arms and legs. Begin moving your hands and feet just a little. And as you continue to breathe deeply, feel all of the energy coming back into your body. And begin to stretch. Using every muscle in your body. Enjoying the refreshment and the relaxation in every muscle of your body. And in your own time, bring all of your awareness back into your body, back into the room. And just as you're ready, gently allow the eyes to open again. Bringing that calm, that peace with you. Spend some time just sitting quietly. Until you're ready to go about your activities.

Chapter Nine

Nutrition and Other Therapies

Much emphasis is placed on what we should eat when we are dealing with a life-threatening disease. No subject is more open to debate, and very often the lay person becomes completely bewildered and confused by conflicting advice. One book will claim the way lies in macrobiotics, whilst another will claim that raw foods are all-important. One propounds the essentials of juices whilst another relies heavily on supplementation with mega-dosages of vitamins.

For the person with a disease, the confusion can become so acute as to cripple all constructive endeavours. Confusion is our worst enemy as it saps our strength.

The premise on which this entire book is based is that peace of mind is our greatest healer and, therefore, our primary goal. Our choice of an appropriate nutritional programme must be in accord with this aim. Many people will practise meditation, visualisation and relaxation techniques to help themselves in establishing a calm and peaceful attitude, only to be thrown into a flap because they are half an hour late with their carrot juice. We need to bring the peace and calmness we experience in our meditations into every other aspect of our lives. Some people put their lives, and their healing, into compartments. 'I'm meditating for my mind and spirit, and I'm sticking to this special programme for my body', instead of having and overall sense of trust and wholeness in their healing process. To experience peace of mind, with regard to nutrition, it is essential you have a programme which:

— you believe is of the utmost benefit to you

— is well within your capabilities in regards to preparation

To decide that our healing lies in personally grown produce picked fresh from our own organically mulched garden, plus wheatgrass, freshly prepared vegetable juices six times a day and homemade bread, when we live alone is unrealistic, to say the least.

I believe it is essential for anyone wishing to adhere to a cleansing yet nourishing diet, for the purpose of assisting in their healing process, to be under the guidance of a qualified and experienced doctor or naturopath. Choose someone whom you trust and who is familiar with working in this particular field. When tailoring this nutritional programme, it is essential to take into account the emotional state, cultural background, religious restrictions, physical condition and personal wishes of the patient *and* the amount of support that person has at home to assist in the prepartion of a special diet. It is essential that you find a diet which will work for *you*, as opposed to a diet which turns your entire household upside down in order to fit *it*.

Diet is only one aspect of an overall approach to healing. Unless wisely guided, a patient will often put more effort into their dietary preparation and other therapies which they have chosen to incorporate, simply because it is something tangible they can 'do' to help themselves. Our society is based on 'doing' rather than the exploration of 'being'. When we are newly diagnosed with a disease, our tendency, after the initial panic has dispersed a little, is to find the things which we can actively 'do' to help ourselves. It is very easy to get lost in the 'doing' and thus overlook the importance of 'being'. A new diet adopted out of fear for the disease will not be nearly as beneficial as one calmly chosen to assist in your healing. Often members of the patient's family see their most useful role as 'the gatherers of information' with regard to diets and other therapies. This is a valuable and necessary role. However, it can still be carried out with calmness. There *is* time: time to assimilate, to talk, discuss, share feelings and consolidate your combined strengths.

Once all the factors mentioned before have been taken into account, a programme can be designed which allows for healthy cleansing of the body whilst also providing optimum nourishment of a kind which can be assimilated by this *particular* person. Two people, the same age, with the same disease, may require two very different nutritional programmes based on the considerations mentioned earlier. These nutritional programmes are not curative of themselves. All healing power lies within the patient. We are endeavouring to provide first-class nourishment of a kind which can be assimilated by the body, so it will be in a position to cleanse and heal itself.

Remember, if we are primarily spirits within bodies, rather than bodies who happen to have spirits, then our approach to healing *must* encompass more than dietary considerations. As long as there are unrecognised and unresolved fears, angers, guilts and resentments and an unhealthy grasping at life, all the carrot juice and diets in the world will be of no avail.

It is of paramount importance that the person have faith in the chosen diet and *enjoy* the food they are eating. Many people make themselves miserable, and create far more stress, by adopting a rigid and unpalatable diet. And yet others may well thrive on exactly the same foods. This highlights the crux of the matter — find the nutritional programme which tastes good to you and which will cleanse and heal your body. As has been stated before, the first and most important aspect of healing is the loving gentleness and regard with which you hold yourself. All healing flows from this.

At the time of my diagnosis, I had been a vegetarian and a meditator for fifteeen years. I had not drunk coffee, tea or alcohol nor consumed any 'suspect substance' in that time and had sustained several long fasts. Though my body was not full of toxicity through the ingestion of impure or 'chemicalised' foods, my mind was certainly suspect! Much of my thinking was extremely rigid and inflexible. In fact, my diet very much reflected my thinking, in that I was unbending in sticking to a rigid dietary programme because I believed it to be to my benefit.

For some time, during my recovery, I was teaching yoga and meditation in some of the most ancient and beautiful monasteries in Italy. An Italian has no concept of a vegetarian or someone who would not drink wine — after all, God made the meat and God made the wine, so why not eat and enjoy? The meals provided within the monasteries were simple and wholesome, but they included chicken or seafood and wine. As I sat there at an ancient table from which countless Franciscan monks had taken their sustenance, I pondered. All those years of rigidity in thinking hadn't helped me a great deal. I had excellent powers of concentration and was accustomed to many hours of meditation without a break — sometimes six hours in the one position. However, what I had been discovering was a need for simple loving kindness and less bother with the externals of *how* I should live. More an openness to life; an acceptance of whatever comes. Allowing more trust in each moment with less need to control. An internal 'yes' to life; even an internal 'yes' to leukaemia and death, if that was to be the outcome. A letting go of having to have it *my* way. So, was it important to maintain the habits of fifteen years?

One may say, in the midst of leukaemia, surely a strict diet would be essential. Or, was it best to let go of the rigidity behind these beliefs and trust that the Universe (or God, if you prefer) had me right in the palm of Its hand and I was indeed loved and supported in whatever I chose to do. I chose this latter course of action and cultivated a gratefulness for whatever the Universe saw fit to place on my plate. For preference, now, I don't buy or cook meat — yet I am grateful when someone has the graciousness to serve me with whatever pleases them.

By this above attitude I am in no way advocating a liberal diet of meat and wine! It is only to illustrate the importance of the *attitude* behind whatever diet you adopt. If my attitude had been, 'Oh, what the heck, I've been eating strictly all these years and now I'm dying, I don't care what I eat; it's not going to make any difference anyway!', then that would be the absolute antithesis of a healthy attitude. I believe, for me, it was far more important to cleanse my mind of its negativity than to be preoccupied with nutrition.

For others, it may be advisable to have the strictest guidelines to follow as far as their nutritional programme is concerned. Some people will only experience peace of mind if they feel their diet is a 'tried and true' healing diet. Whilst, for others, peace of mind will be experienced by making gentle and gradual improvements towards a more nutritious programme.

Many people equate a difficult and rigid diet with the degree to which they want to live. This often reflects a life-long attitude of setting high standards which are almost impossible to achieve. Then we can be self-critical if we don't measure up. Often the underlying thought behind this is 'If I really wanted to live, I would be doing everything 100 per cent.' There we are, failing again! It is so sad to see this thinking in people. They can become so depressed by a seemingly insurmountable obstacle. And yet it is an obstacle entirely created by themselves. Pick your diet, do your utmost, and *trust*.

Another common attitude behind the dietary dilemma is one of bargaining. 'If I pick a really difficult diet, and stick to it; if I meditate for three hours every day; if I take my supplements and treatments, then maybe I will "earn" my recovery.' It comes back to 'If I'm good enough, I'll succeed.'

One young couple exemplifies the extreme to which this can be taken. The wife had a very advanced cancer and her husband had given up his work to take care of her and their young children, both of whom were pre-schoolers. He lovingly prepared her juices and special foods and virtually stood over her as she took her supplements. He always encouraged her to maintain a positive attitude. The whole of the home was dominated by her illness and their positive endeavours to overcome it. However, there were times when she didn't feel up to eating anything, or the thought of a juice made her tummy turn. Driven, no doubt, by his desperation to see his wife recover her health, the husband would insist to her that she wasn't trying hard enough. If she *really* wanted to live, she would make the effort to drink just a little of the juice, or eat a little of the food which he had lovingly prepared. This may sound an extreme situation, but unfortunately it is not. It is a very common trap into which many people fall. And there are many variations upon this trap. They are all born of desperation.

Another lady, in a very similar situation to the one just mentioned, would often just 'sit' in her chair, resting. Her husband would ask her accusingly why she was just sitting there when she could be meditating. Was she thinking positive thoughts while she was sitting there? There are several factors involved in such situations. The husband's way of showing absolute love and support for his wife was to prepare everything he possibly could for her so all she had to do was co-operate and everything would be alright. It gave him a sense of control, a sense of participation, a sense of continuing to care for his wife. He was doing his utmost, why wasn't she? When she rejected the food, he felt she was rejecting him and his attempts to take care of her.

This may sound a bizarre situation to many, but we must remember the tremendous stress to a relationship at this time. As may well be imagined, the tension such an attitude creates is anything but conducive to healing. Often, when we are sick, there are people — such as neighbours, friends or family — who offer assistance. We are sometimes reluctant to avail ourselves of their offers as we like to be 'independent'. The spouse or support person may well feel they want to do *all* the caring for the person who is sick — again, as a way of showing their love. If we can avail ourselves of their offers to cook, pick up the children or groceries, take care of the washing or ironing, or whatever seems to be most helpful, it leaves the support person more freely available to spend time with their loved one.

Some of the diets advocated for the 'cure' of cancer and AIDS almost require a full-time cook to keep up with the endless preparation of foods. If you have the resources and desire to be on such a programme, and, if it doesn't create a stressful home environment, then it may well be suitable and beneficial. However, if your entire day is dominated by a rigid programme of juices and food preparation, and the atmosphere in the home is permeated by stress, then something needs to be changed. Again, it is not the juices or the foods which are at fault, but the attitude *behind* their use.

So, by all means enlist the assistance of those who willingly have offered their services. When our priorities are right, we can relax and trust healing is taking place.

This principle applies in exactly the same way to the various other modalities which you may have encountered. Vitamins, herbals, homeopathics, tissue salts, nutritional supplements, minerals, laetrile, iskador, AL 721, just to name a few of the more popular therapies. As well as these various substances which may be taken *in*to the body, there are a host of other modalities which may be utilised. Reiki, shiatsu, re-birthing, regression therapy, psychotherapy, float tanks, yoga, spiritual or psychic healing — the list goes on and on. Don't forget, peace is our one goal. Choose from the modalities and therapies which come easily into your orbit. Again, it comes back to trusting that the things which you need for your healing are at hand.

In my practice, I rely on good sound nutrition of a kind which can be readily assimilated by the person. This nutritional programme is tailored to the individual, bearing in mind the essentials mentioned earlier in this chapter. In addition to this, I recommend vitamins, minerals and other nutritional supplements designed to improve the overall health and well-being of the patient. I use herbals and homeopathics to alleviate many of the side-effects of the medical treatments the patient may be undergoing, and to relieve the unpleasant symptoms of the disease process.

None of the therapeutic substances which I use are in any way designed to cure the disease. All of them are to assist the patient in creating an ideal 'internal' environment in which healing may take place. If we eat a diet which is nourishing to us and which minimises the stress to our bodies, we are co-operating with our own healing process. For instance, your body may well make excellent use of fish and potatoes. However, if you eat 'fish and chips' — that is, fried in batter and oil — you are creating an unnecessary stress for your liver. It is not only impossible for your body to digest oils which have been heated to a high temperature, but they are positively detrimental to your liver. If you have cancer or any other serious disease, it is advisable to assist the liver in its mammoth job of detoxifying the bloodstream. It certainly isn't helpful to increase the stress on an organ which is already overloaded. It is simple common-sense to work in accord with your body, which is under stress at the outset.

Just as we need assistance in choosing an appropriate nutritional programme, so we need to have any other chosen therapy tailored to meet our needs. To find someone qualified to help you in this area, seek out help amongst other patients, your local hospital, community health centre, your doctor, or your health food store, or ask the Cancer Council or AIDS centre in your district.

As I am always asked about what I prescribe as 'a suitable diet', the following guidelines are included. These guidelines are ones which every individual in the community would benefit from, regardless of their state of health. They are based on sound common-sense and sensible nutritional information. They are general outlines only and, again, if you are seriously ill then find a qualified person to help you use these recommendations to your best advantage.

Foods to Avoid Totally:

Avoid any foods containing

preservatives
colourings
M.S.G. (monosodium glutamate)
artificial flavourings
emulsifiers
stabilisers
added sugar
any other chemical additive

Frozen foods

Avoid frozen foods because they have lost much of their 'vitality' as fresh foods. The exception to this can be made in the interests of expediency and harmony within the home. When you make soups, casseroles or pies you may want to make extra and freeze. I believe it is essential for people to have on hand healthy, easy-to-prepare foods, for those times when you come home late, tired or hassled. There may be times when you aren't up to preparing fresh meals and a store of palatable, on-the-table-in-minutes food is a boon. This may especially apply to people who live alone. Most cities and large towns have vegetarian or 'health' restaurants and you may wish to purchase from them soups, casseroles, vegetarian pies and so on, then freeze them for the occasions mentioned above. Check out the ingredients with the chef before buying. In this way we can streamline our culinary activities and leave more time for ourselves.

Fast foods

There are many 'fast foods' available today which are entirely free of chemical additives and which are nutritious. Most health food stores carry a range of tofu burgers, lentil burgers, tofu sausages and other similar foodstuffs. In the interest of expediency and taste, I believe they are a valuable addition to the diet. Again, these can be frozen, so they are on hand for the times when you choose not to spend a long time in the kitchen. If you have a vegetarian restaurant in your area you may choose to have the staff prepare the occasional meal for you. This will depend on the diet you have adopted. Some good delicatessens have homemade soups and other products which may be entirely suitable for you. Humus is a food made from chickpeas, tahini and garlic and can either be prepared at home or bought fresh from a Lebanese food shop or delicatessen. Make life as simple as possible for yourself. I am not suggesting you live on takeaway or frozen foods, but that you have your priorities right, remembering peace of mind as your major goal.

Canned fruits and vegetables
These are best avoided altogether as much of their valuable vitamin content has been destroyed through the canning process. They have lost their freshness and vitality.

Canned Fish
Salmon and tuna which have been canned are fine unless you have chosen a 100 per cent vegetarian diet. There are no preservatives added in the canning process. Whereas the sterilisation process destroys many vitamins, you are principally eating fish for its protein content. This has not been destroyed.

Packet or processed foods
Avoid these, as they are generally not fresh and have substances added to them to prolong shelf life.

Fatty or fried foods
Avoid these altogether, as they are an unnecessary stress on the liver, are often high in cholesterol, and are of no benefit to the body.

Meats
The addition of meat to your diet will depend very much on the state of your health. Some people, believing cancer thrives on protein, decide to adopt a very low protein diet. This is a little

short-sighted as *every* process in the body is also dependent on protein. In the Western world we tend to rely heavily on meat protein in our diet. This has changed in the last fifteen years quite dramatically, as people have adopted healthier eating patterns. Whether you choose to include meat in your diet will depend on more factors than just your health. For some people, to adopt a totally vegetarian diet could be too radical an approach. They may need to move slowly in that direction.

The problem with red meat is that when it is kept in a dark warm place for any length of time it putrefies. The animals which are accustomed to eating red meat have a very short alimentary tract in comparison with human beings. Lions and tigers have only 5–7 feet of alimentary tract in comparison with ours, which is more than 30 feet long. If red meat 'sits' around in our bowel for a long period of time, the toxins which result from the putrefaction may well enter the bloodstream. Again, this is an unnecessary stress to the body. Food, ideally, will take about 18 hours to pass through our body. In this time, the food is broken down into small enough particles to be assimilated into the bloodstream and the remaining roughage is passed through until it reaches the rectum for elimination. You may want to check your own transit time of food. You can do this by eating some sesame seeds or corn and then keep an eye on the toilet bowl. If transit time is less than 15 hours, it will probably mean you are not holding the food long enough for all its nourishment to be assimilated. If your transit time is longer than 24 hours you may well have a problem with toxicity entering through the bowel wall into the bloodstream. Some drugs will lengthen or shorten this transit time.

White meats do not putrefy like the red meats. I usually recommend the inclusion of deep-sea fish or free-range chicken several times a week, to ensure adequate protein intake. Chicken and fish are best prepared by either grilling or steaming. If you are undergoing medical treatment such as chemotherapy, you must ensure you are having adequate proteins. These proteins will also be provided in plentiful amounts by nuts, pulses, legumes and grains.

Most people will find their taste for red meat diminishes when they are unwell. It is the body's natural knowledge of what is good for it that makes this so. If you have a really strong craving for red meat, choose lamb and eat a hearty green salad with it to provide the extra fibre needed.

Eggs

Avoid eggs laid by miserable chickens. Eggs from happy hens, that is, hens who get to scratch around in the dirt and who eat healthy diets, are certainly preferable. The number of eggs may need to be restricted or eliminated altogether by people who are unwell.

Milk

The consumption of milk is every bit as controversial as the custom of meat-eating. The enzymes involved in the digestion of milk are renin and lactase. These enzymes are present in our bodies as babies, but are all but gone by the time we reach the age of three. Human beings are the only mammals who continue to drink milk after the age of weaning. As we no longer have the necessary enzymes to properly or completely digest milk, I believe we are certainly much better off without it. Milk is a great food for babies who are doing a lot of growing, especially growing bones, but not for adults. Avoid cows' milk altogether. If animal milk is an essential in your diet, replace it with goats' milk. However, my preference is for soy milk. It has nearly the same nutritional value as cow's milk without the detrimental aspects.

To argue about the necessity of cows' milk because of its calcium content is also unfounded. All green leafy vegetables have good quality calcium in a form much easier to assimilate than cows' milk. The calcium in cows' milk is bound up with casein, which makes it very difficult for our bodies to assimilate it. Raw sesame seeds are the richest source of calcium naturally available to us. Most fruits and vegetables contain good amounts of calcium, as do nuts.

Yoghurt

Yoghurt is made from milk and so all of what was said in the previous section applies. Yoghurt, however, does have some redeeming qualities, in that it is already pre-digested — to a certain extent anyway. The only varieties of yoghurts I would recommend are either goats' yoghurt, (preferably) or cows' yoghurt made with the *lactobacillus acidophilus* culture. Many people eat these in vast quantities to 'replace' the gut bacteria. In small quanitities, this practice may be helpful after the use of antibiotics or chemotherapy, both of which destroy the beneficial gut bacteria. For people who have any respiratory complaints or sinus, hayfever or chronic nasal congestion, milk and milk products are best avoided.

Salt

Salt should be used sparingly, if at all. Replace with either coarsely ground sea salt (use a salt grinder) or seasoned salt. The seasoned salt relies on sea salt with the addition of 'salty' herbs, such as parsley or celery.

Vinegar

Vinegar is best avoided, as it is a ferment and it inhibits digestion of starches. Use lemon juice instead.

Breads

Use only whole-grain breads. Many breads are available now from organically grown wheat or rye. It may be preferable for you to use a yeast-free bread, depending on your particular health problem.

Ferments and moulds

These may be best eliminated from your diet altogether, again, depending on your particular health problem. They include foods like Marmite, miso, tamari, soy sauce. Be guided by your practitioner as to the necessity of eliminating them.

Oils

Cold-pressed oils low in saturated fat are the only oils recommended. These may need to be restricted or eliminated altogether, depending on your health.

Butter and margarine

My preference is for butter, but used very sparingly. It may need to be eliminated altogether if you have a liver problem. Sparingly means 1-2 teaspoons per day.

Fresh fruits

An abundance of fresh fruit in your diet is to be encouraged unless you are on a sugar-free diet, in which case you may need to restrict the fruit to three pieces per day. Choose from a wide range of fruits to ensure you acquire all your vitamin and mineral needs.

If you have any problem with nausea or squeamishness in your tummy, then it is very likely oranges will make it worse. Avoid them whilst undergoing chemotherapy. Grapefruit are fine. Also, if you have tumours in the liver, it is best to avoid oranges in any shape or form. If your liver is affected, you will benefit by not having any avocado in your diet also. They are high in oils, which may well antagonise the liver.

Make sure all fruit is ripe when eaten. Wash the fruit thoroughly before eating. If you can easily procure organically grown fruit, so much the better. Never cook fruit, as it renders it an acid food.

Dried fruits

Avoid sulphur-dried fruit. Even though sun-dried fruit doesn't look as appealing to the eye, it is far better for you. Dried-fruits are an extremely concentrated food and are best consumed in small quantities. They may be best avoided if you are on a low-sugar or anti-candida diet.

Vegetables

Use a wide range of vegetables in your diet to ensure you receive all your vitamins and minerals. Use both raw and cooked vegetables. When cooking, they are best prepared by either steaming or dry-baking. The occasional vegetable stir-fry is fine for most people. Use only a teaspoon or two of polyunsaturated oil in the wok, to stop the vegetables from sticking and then rely on the juices from the vegetables to provide the moisture.

Nuts

It is preferable to eat all nuts raw. They are an excellent form of protein and supply good quantities of calcium in a very-easy-to-assimilate form. They are more concentrated than the fruits and vegetables and should not be eaten excessively. They are best avoided by people with liver or bowel complaints. Do not eat roasted nuts.

Seeds

These include sunflower, sesame, pumpkin, poppy and caraway seeds. Seeds, like nuts, are a very concentrated form of protein and are best eaten sparingly. They are best eaten raw, as roasting renders them very acid-forming. Make sure your seeds are fresh.

Crackers or crisp breads

Choose whole-grain crackers or crisp breads which have no preservatives, colourings, cheese, sugar or other chemicals added to them.

Pasta

Whole-wheat pastas are fine. Enquire about the ingredients of freshly made, store-bought pastas.

Honey

For those on a sugar-free or candida diet honey is best avoided. For others, it is important to remember that honey is a very concentrated food and thus must be used sparingly.

Juices

Freshly made vegetable juices are an excellent addition to the diet. With vegetable juices you receive an excellent intake of vitamins, enzymes, minerals, trace elements and other substances in a form which is easy for the body to assimilate. They are palatable, easily made and I find they pick up people's energy levels quicker than anything else. There are very few contra-indications for juices. These include some kinds of diarrhoea (about 1 in 100 people with the HIV who also suffer with diarrhoea will have an unfavourable reaction to the juice) and liver disease (these people need to be carefully monitored in order not to overtax the liver).

Juices should always be freshly prepared. The vegetables do not need to be peeled, though washing them is essential. Drink the juices slowly, mixing them well with the saliva. The following recipe is the one I generally recommend. It is made of:

85 per cent carrot juice
10 per cent beetroot juice (fresh, raw)
5 per cent green juice (made from celery, spinach, outside lettuce leaves, parsley, beet-tops — not if they are limp)

Some people have difficulty with the beetroot and it is advised not to go above 10 per cent unless you really enjoy it. I have found that this juice will help people to remain as healthy as possible whilst undergoing chemotherapy. It seems to minimise the side-effects to quite a remarkable degree. I usually recommend three glasses to be drunk each day, but it depends a little on the individual's health and ability to prepare them.

I prefer vegetable juices above fruit juices, especially for those undergoing chemotherapy or AZT or any other toxic treatment. Fruit juices tend to bring a lot of toxicity into the bloodstream and may cause headaches, dizziness or weakness. Vegetable juices are far more gentle in their cleansing action in the body and these symptoms do not occur with them. For those who are not seriously ill and who enjoy freshly made fruit juices, these may be included. Some people advocate emulsifying the juice with a little oil. Frankly I haven't found any benefit in this practice.

Nausea

Many people encounter nausea or an unsettled feeling in their tummies at some stage during their illness. This nausea may be induced by chemotherapy or AZT or some other recommended treatment, or it may just be part of the disease process. There are some simple measures which may be worth trying to alleviate this problem. One of the most useful of all herbs for such complaints is slippery elm. This is the bark of a tree and has been used for centuries by the American Indians as a gruel for their babies to sooth upset tummies and to nourish them. It puts a slimy or mucilaginous coating over the whole of the gastro-intestinal tract. It is very soothing to the smooth muscle and promotes healing to damaged tissue. It tends to regulate the bowel and is useful for those who suffer with either diarrhoea or constipation. Slippery elm is readily available from any health food store and has no side-effects.

I prefer to use it in powder form as it is the most readily assimilated. It is also available in capsule or tablet form and, for problems occurring lower down in the bowel, these may be used instead of the powder. The powder itself can be mixed with water but I find the easiest way to ingest it is mashed into a little banana, yoghurt or soft fruit. Try mixing 2 heaped teaspoons of the powder in this way, and have it 3 times daily, about 20 minutes before each meal.

If you are having chemotherapy, you might like to take it an hour or two before your treatment is administered and, again, a couple of hours after. Slippery elm mashed into whichever-medium-feels-right-for-you may be the only food which 'sits' happily in your tummy for a day or so around chemotherapy time. This will vary enormously from person to person and will depend also on the side-effects of the chemotherapy. I have found that people who are eating a nutritious diet, who are taking appropriate supplementation of vitamins, drinking the vegetable juices and maintaining a positive outlook, seem to suffer only minimal side-effects from the rather toxic treatments prescribed by their physician.

If the slippery elm does not control the nausea by itself, the addition of homeopathics is bound to do the trick. You will need to see a homeopath/naturopath, though, in order to have these prescribed. They are entirely harmless and are remarkably effective in the control of nausea. There are also homeopathics which stimulate the appetite and which restore tastebuds to their former efficiency.

Joanne, whose story is at the end of this book, recently went on a national television show. She was taking chemotherapy by injection at the time, and, to ensure she experienced no nausea, followed the above guidelines. She received chemotherapy on Monday, Tuesday and Wednesday, flew cross-country for filming on Thursday, and resumed chemotherapy on Friday. She felt completely free of nausea and even the expected 'butterflies' in her tummy were minimal!

These suggestions are not in any way intended to be a 'prescription'. They are suggested only as an effective, natural means of controlling nausea or squeamishness. They are totally without side-effects and, in this way, can be very useful. Some people have quite a marked reaction to the medically prescribed anti-emetics. You may find a combination of both prescribed and natural substances works best for you.

Chapter Ten

Working with Pain

There are many different pains from which human beings may suffer. At its simplest level, we experience pain as something that 'hurts'. It may have many different causes, depending on what kind of pain is being experienced.

Perhaps it is the pain of deprivation. It may be some kind of obvious deprivation as in the loss of a limb, or breast or a physical disfigurement. Or it may be more subtle, as in the loss of an organ or the ability to have children. Many people say they are coming to terms with having cancer but are deeply affected by the loss of their hair, brought about through treatment. It may be the loss of weight which preys upon the mind or the loss of energy. For some, it will be the loss felt by having to stop work.

One lady, a breeder of pedigree dogs, felt she was coping with her illness as long as she was able to groom her favourite dogs each day. It was her measurement of being alive and useful. As she became weaker and less able to perform that function she needed to re-evaluate her situation. Interestingly enough, animals often have a very keen sense of what is happening in their household. The dogs belonging to this lady slept at the foot of her bed in the days before her death and would not leave the bedroom for more than a few minutes at a time. They would frequently nuzzle her hand and whimper softly in apparent bewilderment. She in turn would make comforting sounds back to them. She would often say her dogs were aware of exactly what she was thinking and feeling and she found them a great comfort.

Another woman undergoing very minor surgery was distressed to find that two moles, which the surgeon had earlier confirmed as harmless, had also been removed whilst she was under the anaesthetic. These moles were quite unrelated to the reason for her surgery. The surgeon had explained afterwards he had decided he would 'tidy them up' by removing them, whilst he was working in the general area. Her distress turned to outrage because she felt a liberty had been taken at a time when she was most vulnerable. She had placed her trust in his professional integrity and felt this had been abused. Perhaps it was predictable that the area which she had agreed should have surgery healed very quickly, whilst the wounds left by the removal of the moles took many months.

We may not be feeling the pain of a physical loss and yet our pain can be intense. We may have suffered the loss of those we love, either through death or divorce or simply by moving away from our loved ones. The pain felt by these losses can be deep and unacknowledged — our private pain. This pain is often more intense and makes us feel dispirited because no-one quite understands our personal loss. Emotional pain is something to which we can all relate. Unfulfilled dreams, loss of face, disappointing relationships, lack of success in our chosen career, shattered expectations and so on. We deal with these 'pains' according to our past experiences. For one person, bankruptcy will be a shattering conclusion to all creative endeavours, whilst to another, it will be just another 'educational' step along the way. Likewise, a childhood in which there has been little to build the self-esteem may leave scars which take a lifetime to heal. They may be scars which never heal and which influence the way a person makes all future choices.

There is the pain of separation. A child leaving home, ready to start life on his or her own. Friends or family who move to another town or country. A child going to boarding school. Leaving childhood and entering adolescence.

One pain, often overlooked, is the pain of clinging to life. For some, their ultimate pain will be the final separation of death — the leaving of everything familiar. The leaving of our loved ones. The pain of not seeing our children grow to maturity and beyond. Letting go and trusting that all is well. Leaving a body which has completed its task.

In many ways, physical pain is easier to deal with than pain which is more subtle. Physical pain is generally regarded as an enemy to be avoided at all costs. We go to great lengths in our community to alleviate and avoid pain. However, in retrospect, it is plain to me that many of the greatest traumas and 'pains' in my life were fertile soil for growth and understanding. These 'pains' included months in hospital with extensive reconstructive surgery to my legs as a teenager, the death of my much-loved brother, a divorce and leukaemia — just to name a few of the more potent ones! The understanding and growth these experiences allowed was probably unavailable in any other way.

It is very difficult for people to witness a loved-one's pain. We can empathise but, beyond that, we can feel helpless in our inability to give relief. The pain of our helplessness can be most acute. There are many misunderstandings about pain and its relief. Many people think cancer is synonymous with pain. This is a very mistaken belief, as many people never experience so much as a twinge throughout their illness.

It is true that we can learn much about ourselves through the experience of pain. However, we also need to temper our pursuit of understanding with gentleness and compassion. Unrelenting pain is both exhausting and dispiriting. Even the most positive attitude or resolve weakens when pain is persistent.

Pain is only a symptom of some distress which the body or mind is experiencing, and is a cry for help. And help is needed. Pain should not be ignored. It is essential to thoroughly investigate and deal with its cause. This applies regardless of whether the pain is a physical or emotional one.

Unless emotional pain is dealt with it will erode our peace of mind and ultimately cause stress to our body. Suppressed resentments, angers, jealousies and hurts prevent us from living happy and fulfilled lives and inevitably damage our health. It has become apparent that many patients have suffered some major pain or loss in the six months to two years before the onset of their disease. This observation is not a new revelation. For centuries both doctors and lay people knew that after a major stress, people were much more prone to disease. In the eighteen months previous to my diagnosis, my brother had died, I had moved to a new country to undertake further studies, and had separated from my husband!

In an earlier chapter, 'Techniques for Living', we discussed many ways of dealing with these issues and you may wish to refer to that chapter for further practical assistance. The techniques for forgiveness are particularly useful for past situations which still cause us stress. This implies a willingness to let go of the past and an openness to seeing the situation differently.

As has been said before, physical pain requires investigation so we can learn what its cause actually is. It is a common trap, once we have been diagnosed with a serious disease, to believe every ache and pain is associated with 'the disease'. We forget that we may be suffering from muscular tension, arthritis, indigestion or a tension headache. Immediately we think we may have tumours in the brain, bones or tummy! Rather than worry unnecessarily it is better to find out what the cause of the pain is, and find appropriate treatment.

The mind will conjure up all kinds of frightening answers to our pain and that is far more worrying than knowing exactly what we are dealing with. Remember, a good day's worry is far more exhausting than a good day with an axe. When we know what we are dealing with, we can marshal our resources to work within that situation. The unknown is always more intimidating than the known. It is good to remember, also, that everything seems much worse at 3 a.m. What is quite tolerable in the clear light of day is sometimes overwhelming in the still watches of the night. The feelings of isolation in the middle of the night can be very acute. Sometimes I used to feel everyone was sleeping contentedly in their beds, while I was quietly dying in my room. I was fortunate to have a very understanding mother to whom I could express my fears. Often just being able to talk to a sympathetic friend is sufficient to alleviate the stress associated with our fears and anxieties. Likewise with past resentments, hurts, jealousies and so on. Once aired with an understanding person, they diminish in their intensity. If we don't have such a person in our lives then we may need to enlist the aid of a trained counsellor who can help us to resolve our difficulties.

Some of the other avenues worth exploring for the relief of pain are listed here. It is a matter of trying out different suggestions and finding which ones are most appropriate for you. They are only suggestions which have proved useful for others and are not designed to be 'prescribed'. You may wish to discuss any of the following techniques with your physician before embarking upon them.

THE PAIN SCALE

Using a scale to talk about our pain can be a very useful tool. This means we measure our pain on a scale of 0–10. A zero means we are pain-free, a ten means something really needs to be done about our pain *now*. To 'scale' pain in this way seems to somehow objectify it. It puts it 'out there' for discussion with our carer. After a time we can also learn which number on the scale corresponds with the technique most useful in alleviating it. For instance, a rating of '3' may mean some diversional activity will take care of it. Perhaps a walk in the garden or a game of Scrabble or cards. A '5' may mean it is necessary to practise a particular relaxation technique for its relief, whilst an '8' may mean we need to look for assistance in the form of appropriate analgesics. It will be a very individual scale and will take a little time in order to become familiar with exactly what will help most. Our pain tolerance can vary enormously. Some people have a very high pain threshold, whilst others will experience fear immediately and that will almost 'lock in' their pain and make it all-consuming. Sometimes, if a disease progresses, our tolerance to pain becomes diminished and we require more effective techniques for its control. Factors such as the weather, boredom, fear, or the anticipation of some unpleasant procedure, and so on, can influence how we will experience our pain.

Pain often restricts our activities, both mental and physical, and when boredom is added to pain it becomes much worse. If boredom is a facet of pain, it is helpful to have recourse to activities which stimulate the mind. These may include everything from a walk in the garden, to doing a crossword, to playing Scrabble or listening to a 'talking book'. These 'books' are usually available form your local library. Other activities such as tapestry, cross-stitch and other crafts can be beneficial in this way also.

One man, Brian, gained enormous satisfaction from completing tapestries at a time when his other physical activities were severely limited. He used to travel quite some distance to a store which specialised in tapestries, to make his choice.

MASSAGE

Oftentimes, gentle massage will relieve the symptoms of discomfort and immediately increase ease and mobility. No-one with a serious disease is free of muscular tension. Massage is a wonderful means by which we can release a lot of tension and the vast majority of people find it extremely relaxing and helpful.

If you are seeking professional massage, try to find a therapist who has had experience with people with life-threatening diseases and who is familiar with some of the particular problems associated with them. You may wish to check out the advisability of massage with your doctor. The principal benefits of massage are:

— the relaxation it induces
— the nurturing received
— the improvement in the overall circulation
— the specific relief of any muscular spasms which may be causing pain, discomfort or limited mobility

If you choose to have professional massage do not be afraid to tell the therapist exactly what it is you want.

Let's have a look at the benefits listed above.

The Relaxation

I recommend to people that they look on the time of massage as being their time to let go and deeply relax. It is preferable to do this in silence as chatting to the therapist both distracts and inhibits the full benefits being received. It is an ideal time to practise relaxation techniques. By doing this, we can become acutely aware of the areas in our body which we habitually tense in sympathy with those in which we experience pain. If we can let our muscles dissolve before the therapist's fingers we will experience the most benefit.

The Nurturing

Having a massage can also be a valuable time to learn to let go and actually receive some tender loving care from someone else. It is a time when we are ministered to. Let yourself luxuriate in the feeling of being tenderly looked after by someone who knows how to do that! It is often difficult for us to let ourselves be nurtured. So many of us like always to be in control of our circumstances, and letting someone take over for a while can be quite a new experience. We may feel rather vulnerable when being massaged, especially if we are in pain, and, for this reason, it is essential we have trust in the therapist.

The Circulation

Massage increases the blood flow to the immediate and surrounding areas. With a restored and adequate blood flow, the area then receives both the nutrients and oxygen which the tissues require. It also means toxins from muscular activity or spasm can be effectively eliminated. Parts of the body which are cold and lifeless can be restored to warmth and mobility. As relaxation becomes deeper, the overall blood flow in the body is increased.

The Relief of Muscular Spasm

Hospital beds were never designed for physical relaxation! They are designed almost entirely for the ease of the nurses. Modern technology is gradually improving the situation for both nurse and patient. Of course, it is not just a matter of the bed. If we are hospitalised there are all the added tensions of diagnostic tests, disrupted routines, endless people, noise, hustle and bustle, and frequently unfamiliar and unpalatable 'not-like-mother-used-to-cook' food. Add to this the stress of impending surgery or the anticipation of test results and it is no wonder our muscles are all of a-twitter.

At one of our major hospitals, more than two years ago, I started a voluntary massage programme for people with AIDS. I felt this was necessary because at the time there was — and sadly, still is — so much fear around people who carried the virus. If people could feel loved and nurtured by the healing power of touch then perhaps it would make their stay in hospital less stressful. The first person I massaged was a young fellow of about 18 years and he quietly wept throughout the whole massage. At the end, I asked him if he wanted to talk about what he had experienced. He said no-one had ever touched him like that before. He had only ever been touched because someone had wanted something from him. That made me cry.

After a short time it became apparent that the massage with these people not only gave emotional comfort and support but also relieved many of the painful muscular and neurological symptoms which they were heir to. To witness a young person who, for the first time in weeks, walks unaided to the bathroom, is a joy indeed. These seemingly small events are sometimes our most precious achievements. This young man said, 'Having AIDS I can deal with. Having to be supported by the nurse whilst I have a pee is really distressing.' Life is made up of many small achievements, especially when we are ill. These achievements are the things which kindle and enthuse our hope. They also ensure our feelings of personal dignity.

Most people will say, after a massage in the hospital, it is the best thing that has happened to them since they were admitted. Some massage therapists will visit people in their homes. If you wish to have a therapist visit you in the hospital, it is essential that you receive permission from your doctor first. To check with the doctor is a simple matter of courtesy. And don't forget massage for the support person or carer! Everyone needs nurturing and support, and massage is a great way of having it.

Reflexology, Acupressure and Acupuncture

These modalities work by stimulating the circulation and the energy flow to an area. They can be very helpful in alleviating pain. A trained therapist is usually needed, certainly for acupuncture. However, a therapist may be willing to show the support person the appropriate points to massage so they can bring relief to the patient.

Exercise

A pleasant distraction involving exercise can be helpful in dealing with pain. This may involve a favourite sport or a gentle stroll in the garden. Sometimes all that may be managed is a slow shuffle up and down the hallway. Even quiet exercises done whilst in bed can relieve stiffness and poor circulation.

Ankle rotations, and the tensing and releasing of muscles throughout the body, are helpful for those confined to bed. The support person, or carer, can assist the patient by gently moving the various parts of the body.

For other people, quite vigorous exercise will bring pain relief. One of the effects of vigorous exercise is that we secrete endorphins into the bloodstream. These endorphins are the body's own natural pain relievers. They are also released into the bloodstream when we laugh heartily or when we weep. You may well have experienced the deep relaxation throughout your body after a really good cry.

One man, Peter, who had lung cancer with metastases in the bones found swimming vigorously brought him relief from his pain. He said it was often difficult to get going but once he had 'broken through' the limitation he felt was caused by the pain, he would be able to continue easily for several laps. He was then free of pain for at least a couple of hours.

Another patient, a keen tennis player before her illness, found similar relief when she had a quiet game with her husband. She would play quite slowly at first because of the restriction her pain imposed. After several minutes, though, she would find her mobility increased and she could play more forcibly.

In his book, *Anatomy of an Illness,* Norman Cousins gives a really excellent account of dealing with his painful and crippling disease by the conscious use of laughter. He found 10 minutes of good belly laughter gave him two hours of pain relief. Used in this way, laughter is a form of exercise and one of the most pleasant ones at that! Internal jogging! It is a very inclusive form of exercise and is quite infectious. We don't even need to leave our bed. Funny friends, videos or books can be a godsend. Laughter makes everything much more tolerable and it helps us to keep our perspective. It is one form of exercise in which everyone can participate. Learn to escalate a smile into a chuckle, a chuckle into a laugh, a laugh into a real belly laugh. Our own laughter is a very reassuring sound to our ears!

POETRY

Some people find release from their pain by listening to poetry. Its beauty and imagery can provide a very special oasis for the mind, taking the concentration away from the difficulties of the present. Having someone read to us when we are unwell can be very comforting. Don't overlook the possibility of writing poetry yourself either. This can be a useful means of expression for those whose activities are curtailed.

Music

Like poetry, music can soothe, comfort and uplift us. We can go beyond our pain to a space of calm and peace. One young boy, who had a great deal of pain caused by his cancer, loved to listen to recordings of pan-pipes. He would play them over and over again. Listening to music which is bright, cheerful or inspiring can certainly lift our spirits.

Touch

Like massage, the simple loving touch of someone can bring great comfort. A hand held, a brow softly stroked, a foot gently massaged. These small gestures sometimes convey all that is necessary. To be in pain is stressful by itself. To be in pain and to feel isolated from love is much worse. A gentle hug or caress is one of love's most natural means of expression. By our response to the care and love shown to us we can bring comfort to our carers. It is important for the carers to feel appreciated and that their 'loving' us is acknowledged. A simple smile or returned gesture often speaks more eloquently than words.

Several years ago I was due to fly to America to learn from Gerry Jampolsky and the Center for Attitudinal Healing. He is a well-known doctor whose special interest has been working with people with life-threatening diseases, particularly children. I was planning to be away for only a week. At the time I was working with a young boy who had a very painful prostatic cancer and was nearing death. I had asked Charlie several weeks before how he felt about my going away and he had said it was alright for me to go. In fact, he had said 'There are going to be a lot of children in your life like me. I think you had better go and get your questions answered.' Charlie was nine years old, a fact which I found difficult to remember given his mature outlook. As it turned out, I cancelled the trip just three hours before I was due to fly out of the country. Somehow it didn't feel right to be leaving him or his family right then. The following evening he had a very painful visit to the hospital where doctors performed a bladder irrigation. We worked together to relieve his pain. After it was all over and he was back in his own bed he reached for my hand, smiled, and said 'thanks for staying'. It was all I needed to confirm the 'rightness' of my decision. It was not only right for Charlie that I stayed. It was right for me also. I realised Charlie had provided all the answers to the questions which I was flying to America to ask Gerry.

Prayer and Affirmations

The repetition of a positive statement or the 'offering up' of our pain to a Higher Source can bring comfort and a changed perception of our situation. When we are in pain, at least we know with certainty that we *are* alive. To practise a technique of relaxation at this time can be very challenging. It helps if we have been practising on the 'little pains' before we tackle the more intrusive ones. Once we are in a deeply relaxed state it can be very helpful to quietly repeat a word or phrase which we find comforting. To work with the inward and outward breath adds power to our practice. Some affirmations which have been found useful are:

Let go and let God

All is well

Healing peace

Peace and calm

These words, repeated silently and slowly in the mind, can be rhythmically attached to the breath. For instance, on the inward breath, we can repeat silently 'Let go and . . . ', and on the outward breath, 'Let God', and so on.

These techniques require practice and perseverance. With a strong faith, all things are possible. It even becomes achievable to transmute pain into warmth and joy. It is often the resistance to pain which makes it unbearable, not the pain itself. It is its limiting character which we resist.

As we said earlier, sometimes a really good cry followed by a talk with an understanding friend is all we need, and then we are more easily able to enter a state of relaxation and to use these affirmations.

Breathing Patterns

There are times when we need to 'will' our way through pain. It can be a real effort sometimes to actually go for a walk, or have a swim, or finish 'that job' when we are in pain. And there are other times when we need to stop what we are doing and consciously practise some technique to help alleviate it. Sometimes one approach is just right, other times a different one is needed.

One technique which is enormously valuable is simply breathing! Often when we are in pain it is reflected in the manner in which we breathe. Our breathing can become restricted or laboured. Sometimes we develop the habit of breathing in, holding the breath and take an age to let it out again. Once we detect this pattern we are in a position to establish a healthier rhythm. More often than not, with this sort of breathing, there are some emotional factors at play. Emotions such as fear or uncertaintly. To establish a better rhythm helps to calm those emotions. It can be helpful to adopt a counting method with the breathing. For instance, we may choose to breathe in to the count of 4, hold for 4, and breathe out to the count of 4. We can gradually lengthen the breath so we breathe in to the count of say, 10 or even 12, hold for that long — or a shorter period — and breathe out for the same count. Experiment until you find what works best for you. There is no right or optimum way of 'doing it'. The right or optimum way is the one which works for you.

Another very restful technique is to breathe in and then focus on the little pause at the end of the inward breath. Then breathe out, and again focus on the little pause at the end of the outward breath — each inward and outward breath leading to that comfortable pause. As the mind quietens, the pause naturally lengthens. No effort is required to lengthen it.

Some may find the practice of 'breathing in love, breathing out fear', helpful. With each inward breath, focus on love as you breathe in, and let all fear drain out of the body with the outward breath. One of the practices described at the end of this chapter works to alleviate pain through the use of the breath.

BREATHING WITH THE PERSON IN PAIN

A technique which is very useful when working with people in pain is to breathe with them. This may be done in many ways, according to the relationship which you have with the patient. Choose a technique which is appropriate to that relationship. To look into each other's eyes and begin to breathe at the patient's rhythm is all that is needed. After a short time, a general sense of peace and calm is experienced and the breathing may naturally become slower and deeper. This produces a very close intimacy between the carer and the patient and this may not be appropriate in all situations. Looking into the eyes of another for any length of time inevitably brings an intimacy not experienced in any other way. Many people may find such intimacy makes them feel too vulnerable and, of course, this must be respected.

Even just sitting by the bedside of someone in pain, and breathing according to their own pattern, somehow engenders a feeling of calmness. Very often the patient's breathing deepens and becomes less laboured as their pain and fear decrease. Perhaps the reassurance this practice brings is transferred to the patient and their anxieties or fears are somewhat allayed. It is not necessary for the patient to understand, or even to know, what the carer is doing, for the benefits to be felt. I have practised this with people who are unconscious and whose breathing has conveyed distress. If we remain in a calm and peaceful state whilst breathing with the person in this way, this can have a surprisingly beneficial effect which is reflected in their breathing. I always 'talk' to the person from my heart when involved in this practice. Unspoken words of reassurance have a powerful effect.

Breathing with a patient also helps us to enter into their 'time zone'. It is the most effective way I know of doing so. When we are unwell, or in pain, our perspective on the world is entirely altered and we may well be in a different 'time zone' from everybody else. To have someone who is on their 'world-time zone' rush into our room when we are in a very different one, can be extremely jarring and certainly won't be felt as comforting. I make it a practice, when visiting people in hospital or in their homes, that I always stop before entering their room and take some long, slow, deep breaths to calm and 'centre' myself. In this way I leave 'my world' outside.

Our breathing is our most intimate connection with life. Without breath there is no life. It is the breath which ultimately connects us to our physical existence. If we are in pain and someone takes the time to breathe at *our* rhythm and at *our* depth it may provide reassurance, comfort and confidence that all is well. When there is reassurance, fear diminishes, and pain is more easily tolerated.

The techniques of breathing in harmony with someone in pain, more than any other technique, requires great sensitivity to what is appropriate for the patient. To join with someone in their most intimate connection with life can be very valuable *and* it can also be very intimidating. We are not *doing* something *to* the patient. We are not manipulating the person's experience. We are not even trying to change the person's situation. It is simply that, out of love or care for the patient, we wish to join with them in their experience, to share their reality. This co-joining of two people expands one's reality. It embodies a sharing attitude and the creation of emotional support. In order to use any of these techniques effectively, it is necessary to put aside our own emotions. One cannot enter wholeheartedly into the experience of another whilst being preoccupied with our own situation. When we experience a deep sense of calm and peace within ourselves, we are more able to share in another's reality. If we are panicky and uncertain, it is these feelings which we will bring to the patient. These feelings are likely to create more agitation and an *increase* in pain.

A variation on this breathing technique was extremely helpful to a teenager who had a leg amputated because of bone cancer. Kathy was 18 years old and had been living with cancer for more than three years. Our first encounter was about six weeks before she died. She was being nursed at home by her very devoted family. As she became weaker her tolerance to pain diminished. She had always had a very high pain threshold but with the length of her illness and her overall weakness, each day became more difficult than the preceding one. Kathy experienced quite sudden and severe 'phantom' pains in the amputated leg. Her pain was not constant, but, when it did come, it was increasingly difficult for her to cope. At the first sign of the pain, her mother would prepare an injection of morphine. Kathy's father found the situation terribly distressing and usually had to leave the room. Kathy usually closed her eyes, tensed all her muscles and waited for the pain to pass. Initially I was also terribly distressed. Then, after a discussion with Kathy, she and I decided to see if we could 'breathe' our way through this pain together. With the next wave of pain, we joined hands, looked into each other's eyes and breathed together in harmony. We used a kind of panting breath, similar to that taught to mothers for use throughout labour contractions during childbirth. It was a lovely experience for both of us because we found we could 'connect' with each other at a depth not normally experienced. In this 'connectedness' even the pain was tolerable and before long morphine became unnecessary. The atmosphere in the home became calmer. Other members of the family also tried this practice with her. Everyone benefited. They had found a skill and strength within themselves which enabled them to overcome a previously insurmountable obstacle. Instead of the situation becoming one in which the family dissolved into their own separate modes of survival, it became a time of joining together. Kathy's pain diminished, not only in severity but also in frequency.

Developing techniques to assist us through the difficulties inherent in illness gives us a sense of being in control of our experience. These skills are the very antithesis of chaos and helplessness. From the pratice of these skills we learn that even though life has its difficulties, its problems *are* surmountable.

THE ROLE OF ANALGESICS

It is a common, yet erroneous, belief that taking medical analgesics will somehow interfere with the process of healing. I have seen people who haven't slept for days and who are dispirited and depressed through continuous pain, because they refuse to take any prescribed medication. This is a really short-sighted view. Whilst the body is in pain, very little healing can take place, as all one's energy goes into dealing with it. Constant pain is very debilitating and it is difficult to keep one's spirits up when it is relentless. Often, all that is needed is 48 hours of good pain relief in which the patient gets some sound sleep. After this time, the medication can often cease. Once we are rested and our spirits are up again, everything becomes easier. This pain-relief programme needs to be administered by someone who is entirely competent to do so.

Some people are concerned that if they go onto a strong analgesic like morphine they will become addicted. Some fear that if they are taking morphine then their 'end' must be close. Often these fears are held more by the surrounding family than by the patient. They are all understandable anxieties. With proper explanation from your prescribing physician these anxieties are easily eliminated. The technique described above, whereby strong analgesics are given for a short period of time, does not result in addiction. On the contrary, it results in a contented person who has gained some valuable rest and whose spirits are restored.

If pain is chronic and is being managed routinely by analgesics then, again, they must be competently prescribed and administered. There are often 'pain clinics' attached to hospitals. These clinics specialise in appropriate pain management. Often the analgesics prescribed are correct but the administration technique is at fault, and these clinics can certainly assist with relevant information.

Many of the more powerful analgesics are given on a routine basis, rather than on the basis of 'pain demand'. If they are given every four hours, for instance, the patient may well not experience strong pain. If you wait for the pain to come before administration of analgesics, it takes much longer for them to be effective.

One of the most common problems people find with prescribed analgesics is their constipating effect. The person prescribing appropriate pain management should understand this and make sure adequate precautions are taken to alleviate this unnecessary complication. Constipation can cause more distress than the pain! Dietary factors, appropriate to the person's needs, can also be useful.

In some instances your physician may suggest a more radical treatment for adequate pain management. This may involve direct intervention at the nerve supply to the painful area. If this proved necessary, your doctor will discuss the procedure extensively with you so that you understand exactly what it may entail.

VITAMIN C AND COFFEE ENEMAS

These two forms of pain control are considered controversial, so far as their effectiveness is concerned. There are many people who claim to have had pain relief through the frequent administration of high dosages of Vitamin C. These dosages may be taken orally or intravenously. Obviously, the administration of Vitamin C directly into the bloodstream may only be performed by a willing doctor. It is also essential to have your doctor's permission for the use of coffee enemas.

Oral dosage of Vitamin C needs to be administered on a very individual basis as everyone's demand for it varies. Coffee enemas have also been found very useful by many people to assist in their pain control. For some people the very idea of a coffee enema, is just not their cup of tea! The benefits of the coffee enema are usually experienced about 20 minutes after administration. If you decide to try them out for yourself I suggest you be under the guidance of someone who is experienced in their use.

The following 'recipe' is the one I have found most useful:

Place 2–3 heaped tablespoons of freshly ground coffee into a saucepan with one pint of boiling water. Simmer for 10 minutes. Let cool to body temperature. Strain into an enema bag. This is then gravity fed into the bowel. It is best to lie on the left hand side whilst the enema is being introduced. You may then like to lie on your back for the next half hour and then evacuate the bowel.

Many patients with liver cancer have successfully controlled their pain solely through the use of coffee enemas. For some people, these enemas are effective if given 2–3 times daily, whilst others will benefit by having them more frequently, up to 6 per day. It is advisable to check with your doctor about the possibility of using coffee enemas. Do not expect an enthusiastic response, as your doctor will probably never have heard of them. Usually the only contra-indication is if there is any perforation in the lower bowel. Coffee enemas first became popular as part of the Gerson programme for cancer patients.

TECHNIQUES OF RELAXATION FOR PAIN RELIEF

The following relaxation techniques are extremely helpful in pain relief and control. The first one is an exploration of the nature of pain and a breathing technique which assists us in 'dissolving' it. This exercise takes one right into the heart of the pain so we may learn from it and understand what its nature actually is.

The second technique is an ancient yoga practice in which we rotate our awareness throughout the body. In this exercise we shift the focus of our attention from one part of our body to the next and so on. Initially, during the exercise, the pain may seem to increase before it subsides. Both these techniques are valuable and it is a matter of personal preference as to which one is the most suitable. Try them both. Practise them on a regular basis to achieve the greatest benefit.

I have put both these techniques on a cassette tape which is available from the address at the back of this book. You may wish to read these exercises onto a tape for yourself. It is very beneficial to have someone talk you through them. Or, perhaps a friend or carer could read them to you. They *must* be read very slowly. The more these techniques are practised, the more adept you will become with your pain control.

Exercise One

(To be read very *slowly by a friend)*

Find a position, either lying down or sitting, wherein you can be as comfortable as possible.

Begin by taking a few slow, deep soft breaths as you let your body settle into its position. Let yourself settle into your body, bringing your awareness into your body.

Gently allow the awareness to focus on the area of pain in the body. Feel the sensations in that area, and allow the body, the tissues, to soften around the area of sensation.

A listening, an openness, a softening in that area. Opening and softening. No restriction or pulling back. Just opening and softening. The tissues softening, letting go of the sensations in that area. Letting them float free. Ligaments softening. Muscles softening. No resistance to the pain. Let the pain just be there without resistance. The tissues softening all about the pain. Opening up more and more. Allow the pain to float freely in the body. Not holding on. Not resisting. Gently opening up to the moment of sensation.

Each moment of awareness extending. Vast awareness. The sensations floating free in this vast awareness. The body floating free in this vast awareness.

The body full of space, without tension, without holding onto anything. Just space, just awareness floating free.

Each moment softening the body, releasing tension. Without contraction. Feeling its way into greater openness, greater space. Letting go all around the area of sensation.

The cells, tissues — even the bones — opening, softening, yielding. Allow the whole body to soften, to yield, to open into space, into the moment.

Bring the awareness to the breath. Savour each breath. Letting the breath breathe itself. Open and soften the awareness around the breath, as if each breath is the first, each breath is new. Not changing or judging the breath. Just allowing each breath to be as it is.

Allow the same awareness with the thoughts which drift into the mind. Not resisting, not judging. Allow them to float through the awareness as they will.

The feelings which arise. Allow them to float freely through the awareness without restriction. Just another sensation, another awareness, another moment.

Each moment just as it is. Each moment received fully. The mind soft, open, yielding, receiving whatever is there. If there is thought, let it come, to pass. Not wishing to change it, to be shielded from it.

If there is feeling, let it come, to pass. Just openness, willingness to have that feeling. And to let it pass. A willingness to be, a willingness to experience. Each moment full and rich with experience.

Allow the body to be open and soft and fluid. Like an ocean. Each sensation floating gently to the surface. Exploring each sensation with gentleness and openness. Let any rigidity melt away into the ocean of awareness.

The edges in the body becoming soft and fluid. The borders within the body dissolving. Softening. Letting go of contraction. Floating free.

Now gently bring the awareness to the pain. Staying soft, still open, without tightening. Bring the awareness to the very centre of the pain.

Allow the experience to be fully there, without resistance.

Take a moment to explore this sensation, to explore its reality. What shape does this sensation have? Going right to the centre of this sensation.

Is it angular?

Is it rounded? Not resisting the experience of this sensation. Just a gently probing into its nature.

Does this shape, this sensation have a temperature?

Is it hot or is it a cold sensation?

Is it a very large sensation, or quite small and pointed? Letting each wave of sensation have its time. Not holding back. Gently investigating this sensation.

Is it fixed in one place?

Or does it move?

Is it round and hard, like a ball, or is it soft and flat?

Does it pulsate throughout the area, or is it still and quiet? Allow the sensations to gently ripple through your awareness. Being open to each sensation, to each nuance of sensation. Let your awareness become full of the sensations. Until awareness becomes one with the experience. Letting go, flowing with each moment. Allowing the changes in each moment. Savouring each moment of sensation.

A state of careful listening. Listening to each moment as it unfolds. Not anticipating, not drawing back. Just present, being united with each moment as it unfolds.

Is this sensation heavy or light?

Is it solid and stable or like a mist, constantly changing and moving?

Soft, open awareness. Exploring. Notice any resistance, any tension in mind or body. Let go, soften. Allowing an openness to each unfolding moment. Let each sensation come, to pass. Gently opening up to the very centre of sensation, to its very heart.

Is it tingling? Dull?

A soft or hard pressure? Every moment new. Each one changing.

Is it heavy and dull? Or is it bright and fiery?

What colour does it have? Investigate each moment with a soft open mind. With a willingness to experience and explore.

Now gently direct the breath to wash around the sensation. Gently washing around the sensation as a wave washes around a pebble on the shore. The ebb and flow of the wave, like the ebb and flow of the breath. Gently, softly washing around the shape. Softening its edges. Soothing and softening as it gently washes around the sensation. Without forcing, without effort. Each breath soft and gentle.

Then allow each breath to wash right through the centre of this sensation. Opening up right into the centre of this sensation. Letting space and ease flow right to its centre. Each breath flowing easily to its centre.

Feel the easy flow of each breath. Feel the softness, the relaxation throughout the whole body. Each cell soft and open.

(long pause)

And, in your own time allow your eyes to gently open.

Exercise Two: *Rotation of awareness around the body*

(To be read slowly, by a friend)

Lie down comfortably on the floor or on a mattress with a small pillow to support your head. If you need to change your position slightly during this exercise, do so and return to your practice. It is important to be as comfortable as possible throughout this practice and yet to cultivate a quietness within your body, so let the movements be minimal.

Allow the eyes to close over lightly. If your breathing is easy and comfortable then breathe through your nose, keeping your mouth closed. Begin by taking some long slow deep breaths. With each outward breath let go of all tension and anxieties.

Feel them drift out of your body with each outward breath. Then allow your breathing to return to its own natural relaxed rhythm. Softly in, softly out.

Devote this next little while to your practice of this technique. Without opening your eyes, become aware of the room in which you are lying. Allow all the impressions within the room to enter into your awareness. Then take your awareness outside of the room and allow all the sounds — all the impressions — to float through your consciousness. Not holding onto them. Not judging or critcising. Just allowing them to float into and out of your awareness.

Now bring all of your awareness into your body. Become aware of your body. Each part of your body coming into your awareness. Let the awareness merge with the body. At one with the body. Feeling the body as a whole. A living, breathing awareness. Let your awareness rotate around the body. As each part of your body is mentioned, bring your awareness to that particular part and actually feel that area. Not thinking about the area, actually feeling it.

*******Bring your awareness to your right thumb. Index finger. Middle finger. Ring finger. Small finger. Palm. Wrist. Lower arm. Elbow. Upper arm. Shoulder. Armpit. Right side. Waist. Hip. Thigh. Knee. Calf muscle. Ankle. Heel. Sole. Right big toe. Second toe. Third. Fourth. And little toe.*

Take your awareness to the left side of your body. Become aware of the left-hand thumb. Index finger. Middle finger. Ring finger. Small finger. Palm. Wrist. Lower arm. Elbow. Upper arm. Shoulder. Armpit. Left side. Waist. Hip. Thigh. Knee. Calf muscle. Ankle. Heel. Sole. Left big toe. Second. Third. Fourth and fifth. Right buttock. Left buttock. Small of the back. Right side of the back. Left side of the back. Centre of the back. Shoulders. Right shoulder blade. Left shoulder blade. Back of the neck. Back of the head. Crown of the head. The forehead. Right ear. Left ear. Right temple. Left temple. Right eyebrow. Left eyebrow. The space between the eyebrows. Right eye. Left eye. Right cheek. Left cheek. Nose. Tip of the nose. Lips. Chin. Throat. Collar bones. Chest. Stomach. Abdomen. Navel. The whole front of the body. The whole of the back and the whole body. Become aware of the whole body. The body as a whole.

Resting on the floor or mattress. The whole body resting on the floor or mattress and breathing normally.

*(Repeat from ** then continue)*

Effortlessly. Become aware of the whole body resting on the floor or mattress and breathing effortlessly.

Imagine that you are standing above the head of your body and are looking down onto your whole body.

Be fully aware of your whole body. Your awareness fully absorbed by your whole body. Merging with your whole body. Your body and your awareness at one.

Now bring your awareness to the place where your body touches the floor or mattress.

Feeling the pressure of the surface against your body.

Let your awareness spread beyond your bodily sensations. Expanding your awareness of the floor or mattress right out to its perimeters. And beyond. Let the awareness of all sounds, sensations and impressions float through your consciousness. All sounds rising out of, and falling into, stillness. Awareness of all objects within your environment. Aware of your body and your external environment.

(Long pause)

Now gently bring your awareness back into your body. Feel its weight and posture. Feel where the body rests on the floor or mattress. Allow your breathing to deepen. Enjoy the sensation of the breath flowing in and out of your body. As you breathe in, feel the energy flowing back into your body. The muscle tone returning to your arms and legs. Begin moving your toes. Your feet. Your fingers and hands. Gently stretching. Continue to stretch your whole body. Enjoying the refreshment, the relaxation throughout your body. In your own time, just as you're ready, gently allow your eyes to open. You may wish to close them again, rest, and open them when you're ready. When you are ready to move, do so with gentleness and care for your body.

Chapter Eleven

Living with the HIV

Although this book is chiefly directed to people who have either developed AIDS, cancer, or some other life-threatening disease, and those caring for them, there is much information contained within its pages which will assist those affected by the *potential* of a life-threatening disease. It is my belief, and my hope, that through the implementation of the techniques and philosophy contained within this book, people who are symptom-free, but infected with the HIV, will maintain and improve their health. This chapter is directed to those people who are infected and who may or may not be experiencing any of the symptoms associated with the syndrome.

Over the past four and a half years, I have worked with about five hundred people who are infected. The modes of transmission have varied enormously, as have the lifestyles of those affected. There have been many different people who have received contaminated blood. Heroin addicts who have shared needles. Haemophiliacs of varying ages. Children born of infected mothers. Young men living in the fast lane of gay bars. Women who had a 'one-night stand' with men they didn't know were bisexual or drug users. Prisoners who have become infected within our gaols. Husbands who have led a secret life of bisexuality, unknown to their wives. Those who have been sexually active, and those who have had very few sexual partners.

Regardless of the mode of infection, whether through sexual or non-sexual activity, the issues and guidelines for staying well are the same. The concept of guilt or innocence is irrelevant and has no place here or anywhere.

The initial reaction to the diagnosis may be one of denial, anger, or blame. Even before these reactions, there will undoubtedly be shock. To have these feelings is entirely natural. However, to get stuck with them is detrimental to your peace of mind — and therefore your health. A calm and positive attitude will be your greatest ally in staying well. If we have feelings of guilt because of our sexual preferences, or perhaps anger because we feel we are 'innocent', then we must work with these emotions and the attitudes from which they spring. Then we are able to move on to take full responsibility for our health and our perception of our situation.

Each person must find their own path to healing and wholeness. Health is peace of mind. With peace of mind as our main goal, we also create the perfect environment in which our physical body can achieve and maintain health.

There is substantial evidence emerging that only a proportion of infected people may go on to develop AIDS. The problem becomes understanding what it is that creates the environment in which the virus flourishes. Or, conversely, to study the means by which we can make it very difficult for the virus to successfully reproduce within our immune system, and — by utilising these means — stay well. Those who seem to be most susceptible to the virus flourishing are those with depressed immune systems. The immune systems may have become depressed for many reasons other than infection with the HIV. There may be many other factors which can weaken our ability to respond fully to the presence of the virus. Perhaps there have been other viral infections which have damaged the immune system or specific organs within the body, one or more of the many parasites especially prevalent in the gay community; fungal or bacterial infections; stress from one's pace of life, from recreational drugs, poor self-esteem, poor nutrition, abuse of alcohol or sexual activities — all these present a potent stress to our body's defence system.

Many young people, in their early twenties and younger, feel there is nothing left in life for them to experience. I am always reminded of how precious life is when faced with someone who values it so lightly. The only healing possible for some of these people comes from a loving understanding, reaching out and touching another's painful heart with respect and gentleness. Sometimes the illness is not the infection of the body with the HIV but the total sapping of a spirit which has become full of pain and disillusionment. The spirit must be addressed before one can even begin with the body. To talk to a young adolescent who lives on the streets and is infected by the HIV about the value of carrot juice is to greatly overlook the fundamentals.

We, as a society, have created the environments in which people in our community can feel very isolated — even rejected. It is our responsibility to correct this situation through compassion and practical assistance. In this way our society becomes healed of its prejudices, judgements and aloofness in the face of genuine need.

For some, the mere possibility of others knowing they are infected with the HIV is an incredible stress. They suspect their friends, workmates and acquaintances — even family — will reject or avoid them. Sadly, this is sometimes quite true. This rejection or avoidance can come at a time when we particularly need the love and support of those around us.

A common initial reaction to diagnosis of the virus is one of hopelessness. Many people confuse being infected with the virus with having developed AIDS. Members of the media have done little to distinguish or educate people about the stages of the virus. Newspapers, television and radio thrive on being dramatic. Grim faces give us grim figures and predictions. No-one can live long without hope: it is an essential ingredient of life. The attitude of hopelessness can often hasten the deterioration of a body affected by a life-threatening disease. Remember, undue stress can certainly depress our immune system. Almost all 'fatal' diseases have had survivors, so even those who develop AIDS can still maintain and nurture hope. There is a growing number of people who *are* maintaining and improving their health, even though they have been classified as having AIDS. They are living enriching lives which are of value to themselves and to others. Sometimes their doctors 'reassure' them that they will still die of the disease. It can be difficult to maintain optimism in the face of such discouraging 'reassurance'. So it is vital to find a doctor who will hold out hope and encouragement. We need to take the virus seriously, and it's true, for some, infection may well lead to serious disease and death. However, that should not stop us from optimising our health and emotional well-being.

For those who are in good health, whose spirits are intact and who wish to optimise their health in the face of infection with the HIV, these following areas seem to be the ones most worthy of investigation:

Choose a Technique which will Help you Establish Peace of Mind

The changes suggested to ensure your continued, and indeed, improved health, will require considerable effort in their implementation. Techniques by which you control and focus the mind can be very helpful in strengthening your commitment to change. The regular practice of some agreeable technique can help you establish a routine in a positive direction. We can greatly benefit from participating with a group of people whose ideals and goals are the same. The meditation and visualisation chapters in this book will give you guidelines and techniques which may prove useful to you.

For some people, choosing a technique which embodies a spiritual path may be best. It is a personal choice. As I have said in the main part of this book, it is my firm belief that we are primarily spirit within a body, rather than bodies which happen to have a 'spiritual aspect'. Faith in God, or our spiritual path, can be a powerful ally, especially when we are facing the potential of a life-threatening disease.

Some people may prefer to practise techniques which calm the mind through disciplined movements of the body — as in Yoga, Tai Chi, Aikido or other martial arts. The importance of a calm and positive attitude cannot be overestimated. A positive attitude can only be maintained when we are willing to look at our situation and then consciously *choose* to remain positive. It is not a matter of burying our head in the sand, vaguely expecting everything to be 'fine'. It is a dynamic state of being in which we choose the things we wish to incorporate into our lifestyle in order to stay well.

Taking Responsibility

You may find the lifestyle you were leading up to the time of diagnosis was not really conducive to your health and well-being. You may wish to evaluate it and find new expression for your talents, emotions, ideas, behaviour and sexuality.

Once infected with the virus, it is essential you practise 'safe sex'. That is, ensuring that you, or your partner use a condom *every* time you have sex. Even if the other partner is infected it is essential, as multiple infection can precipitate the activity of the virus. There are many strains of the virus and it appears that if people are infected with more than one strain they may be more susceptible to activating the virus.

Some very simply measures will ensure that you do not infect any other person. Don't share toothbrushes, razors or needles. If you do share needles, clean your equipment in bleach or alcohol. You can infect another person if you practise unsafe sex whether you are engaged in anal or vaginal sex. You can't pass it on by hugging, kissing, sharing plates and cups, sneezing or coughing or through swimming pools or mosquitoes.

Perhaps your job is too stressful or uninteresting, and you may wish to seek a more conducive environment, away from air-conditioning, office politics or other stresses. Party energy may need to be replaced by a gentler, more caring lifestyle which has its foundations in simplicity. Sexual energy may be better transformed into healing energy.

Taking a responsible attitude may include appropriate legal guidance. It may be wise to face the possibility of death and to prepare for it in a responsible manner. Everyone should have a will. This is not morbid; it is good advice, which any competent lawyer would give you. The chapter entitled, 'When do we stop Living and Start Dying?' which follows, has many valuable practical details. There is a chance you will become ill and die from the effects of this virus and it is wise to allow for this fact. Once you have accomplished the legal necessities, it is advisable to drop all thoughts of illness and death.

As for your medical monitoring, choose a doctor in whom you have confidence. If possible, find a physician who is in accord with holistic approaches and who encourages you in your own efforts. Because of the nature of this virus, we should not expect any *one* person to have all the answers. Choose a physician who can understand this. Practitioners from many modalities may have keys for you, and it is not a healthy attitude to hand over responsibility to another person, expecting them to be in charge of your health. The only person who should rightfully be responsible for your health and well-being is you.

It is essential to create your own emotional support system, particularly just after diagnosis. It can be very helpful to meet with others in a similar situation. Cancer or AIDS support groups can be valuable, both emotionally as well as a resource group. You may discover through other participants, just who are the best therapists in your area, who may be able to assist you with diet and supplements or meditation. Also, there may be people you wish to include in the knowledge of your infection and others whom you wish to exclude. Take your time in making those choices. To have good communication with someone who is emotionally supportive to you is invaluable. This may be a lover, friend, family member, support group, therapist, or the friendly voice of a counsellor on the other end of a telephone.

MAKE GOALS

Your goals and desires may change considerably on diagnosis. Most people find relationships with other people become very important. Our goals may include the deepening of our relationships with loved ones. It may be that in looking at your life you can see areas in which you are not satisified, and you can begin to work on these. Your goals may include:

- *to find peace of mind*
- *to stay well*
- *to find meaning in life*
- *to find love*
- *to learn how to love*
- *to find a worthwhile vocation or function in life*
- *to find joy*
- *to improve your physical fitness*
- *to eliminate junk foods*
- *to move to the country or take up a long-desired hobby*
- *to heal past relationships*
- *to create a healthier lifestyle*
- *to stop unnecessary drugs*
- *to exercise regularly*
- *to become an 'expert' about your own body, mind and emotions*

Having goals is basic to our happiness and our feelings of hope. They may be small achievements or mammoth ones. Life is made up of many goals and by achieving them we affirm trust in our own abilities. From time to time, take the opportunity to acknowledge the goals you *have* achieved and give yourself the pat on the back you deserve. We do not always readily recognise our own achievements. Keeping a journal can be very helpful in charting our progress along the way to our anticipated goal. A journal, used in this way, gives a picture of our emotional world — our hopes, desires, goals. Let your journal reflect your private journey to the fulfilment of your goals.

CREATE A HEALTHY LIFESTYLE

A healthy lifestyle encompasses many aspects. It is recommended you get some sound nutritional advice from someone who is qualified to give it. Food allergies may need investigating. So will any parasitic, fungal, bacterial or viral infections, as these may certainly be co-factors in the progression of disease.

If you have a problem with candida albicans, a yeast-like fungus, you will need to approach this problem from a dietary standpoint as well as the prescribed use of effective anti-fungals. Vitamin supplements are also helpful in maintaining and increasing your level of health. Again, find someone who is experienced and competent to help you in the choice of supplements *you* need.

Many have found intravenous Vitamin C therapy to be invaluable, particularly those people whose immune system is under threat from another form of virus or bacteria. Speak to a doctor who is familiar with this type of therapy to see if it may have application to your particular situation. Exercise should be regular, enjoyable and effective. Aerobic exercise which gets you breathing deeply and increases your pulse rate is preferable.

It is very important you take sufficient time to rest adequately, Sleep at night should be sound and undisturbed. If it isn't, correct it by learning techniques of relaxation or, perhaps, by taking some herbal formula to help in re-establishing a good sleeping pattern. A 'sleep tape' can also be valuable for people who are chronic insomniacs (see tapes listed at the end of the book). Build up your exercise programme gradually and don't fall into the trap of over-extending yourself.

Read literature and mix with people who are health-conscious and who are embarking on a programme like yourself. Avoid reading newspapers or listening to television or radio when there is sensationalistic news about AIDS. Rarely is there anything inspiring or encouraging written up, or spoken of, through these avenues. A thirty-second item containing discouraging news can send spirits plummeting for days. Again, practise 'safe sex'. This applies to everyone, whether in a monogamous relationship or not.

Find activities and relationships which give satisfaction and meaning to your life. If you feel isolated or lonely, actively go out to find supportive groups or friends. Consider creating a support group in your area — the chapter on support groups contains everything you need to know about how they can be started and effectively run. A note of caution on support groups, however. Some groups seem to have as their basis a desire to help you die peacefully. Avoid them like the plague! Make sure the aims of the support group you choose to attend has, at its foundation, the goal of helping you to maximise your life in every way possible.

Above all else, learn to love, respect and nurture yourself. Surround your body, mind and spirit with everything required for abundant peace and health. Find time to engage in Nature and drink in its beauty and harmony. If possible, fill your home with fresh flowers, sunshine and fresh air. Simple things like a clean and tidy home or fresh linen on the bed or table, can bring peace and calmness to our day. Such things reflect back to us our own self-worth and self-respect. Listen to music which enlivens and inspires you. Likewise, read literature which gives enthusiasm to your own endeavours.

Once you have adopted a programme which you feel confident and comfortable with, trust that health in abundance is on its way to you. Do not let any symptoms which may present themselves become chronic. Diarrhoea, night sweats, nausea, constipation, bloatedness, lack of energy, poor appetite, rashes — all need investigation. Once investigated they should be treated to eliminate their draining influence on the body — not to mention our spirits.

Find the balance between taking responsibility for your health and your life without it becoming obsessive. On the one hand, I don't recommend people spending their lives looking through the eyes of HIV positivity, but, on the other hand we need to take a realistic and responsible attitude towards maintaining our health. Every day, more and more information is being revealed about effective means by which those people who are infected can increase their overall health. Be open to the new information as it comes, and incorporate what feels appropriate for you. Listen to the still small voice within and learn to trust in your own innate knowing of what is best for you.

Much of what is written in this book applies equally to those who are infected and those with no disease. Read its contents several times, digest what is said, then incorporate what feels good for you.

Through infection we have the possibility to reassess our lives and make fundamental changes to our beliefs, our relationships, our way of conducting our life. HIV can be viewed as a catastrophe or as an opportunity which enables us to review our lives and make the rest of our days — no matter how many — rich with the experience of living a life of deep satisfaction and fulfilment.

Chapter Twelve

At What Point Do We Stop Living and Start Dying?

Michael first came to see me accompanied by his father. He had been diagnosed with a brain tumour two years before. The family had hoped the treatment he had undergone at the time of diagnosis had been successful and that they could resume their lives undisturbed. However, this was not to be, and in the six months prior to when I first saw him he had completed another course of chemotherapy. The doctors were not optimistic for his survival as the tumour had only partly responded to the treatment.

Michael was a student of economics at university and was extremely popular and well-liked by both his fellow students and the lecturers. His symptoms had made it somewhat difficult for him to adhere to any particular diet as his vision and balance were affected and he felt nauseous most of the time. To a large extent we were able to control his nausea. This was accomplished through some dietary changes and through the use of the herb slippery elm, digestive enzymes and homeopathics. (The traditional anti-nausea drugs had exacerbated his 'jitteryness' and imbalance.) Once these symptoms were more under control, Michael was able to resume his studies and go on to a more suitable diet. He began attending our weekly support groups which were held during the day, and arranged with his lecturers that he would be slightly late for his classes so that he could attend these groups. His courage, understanding and sense of humour always brought insight and lightness to our meetings and he became a much-loved member of the group. Many a time, he would weave his unsteady way up the stairs, to collapse in a forlorn heap, struggling to regain his breath. By this time his tumour had spread to other parts of his body, particularly the lungs. His vision had also been seriously affected and he was plagued by flashing lights on the periphery of his visual field. However, he spent more and more of his time in meditation as through this practice he seemed to gain a real experience of peace.

During the weeks before his death, Michael used the groups as an airing ground for his fears, uncertainties and hopes for life beyond death. By exploring these thoughts and concepts with the group, he gained enough strength and courage to include his family in the fullness of his experience. He showed them how they could let themselves be completely open to their own fears and grief, and yet still be full of hope — hope for a recovery, hope that all was unfolding as it should, hope in life continuing through the experience of death, hope in the experience of peace.

Michael had a passion for classical music and attending concerts was one of his favourite activities. The week he died, he attended the support group as usual. He had taken on a kind of radiant, translucent quality and seemed already to have partly left us. His humour was still at the forefront. He was quiet, peaceful, soft and open to each unfolding experience. The visual flashes which had caused him so much distress had vanished, as had all nausea.

He told us he felt healed of all the pain he had experienced. As physical pain had never seemed to be a problem, I probed a little. He replied that he meant all the pain he had felt in his heart; the pain of wanting things to be different; the pain he had felt for family; the pain of resisting life.

The following evening he attended a concert where one of his favourite composers was featured, and the next evening he died — at home with his family. Though there was much sadness at his passing, it would be wrong to say that sadness was the only emotion present. There was also peace and acceptance and even a kind of joy at his release.

One of the things that Michael's story illustrates so well is that there are no dying people. We are either alive or we are dead. At what stage did Michael start dying? Was he living or dying when he attended the group on Monday? Was he dying when he attended the concert the following evening? My belief is we live right through the process of dying. We shed a body, and continue. Leaving the body marks an exit out of one life and a birth into another. Having been privileged to be with so many people when they are undergoing this process, I am assured they are simply moving into some other dimension. I use the word 'assured' because many of the people have told me of 'light' they see, or a 'peace' they feel which seems to fill them with wonder and joy. One teenager who was particularly fearful of dying said just minutes before he died, 'Why didn't someone tell me how beautiful the light was? If I'd known, I wouldn't have been scared.'

There are many accounts of people who have clinically 'died' and have been brought back to life. Many of them speak of the peace and light they experienced. Some describe a tunnel with light at the end. Some 'see' people whom they loved, who had previously died, waiting to greet them on the 'other side'. Many describe some 'being of light' whom they felt emanated tremendous love for them, waiting to welcome them. These happenings are not confined to people with religious or spiritual backgrounds. Many people with no expectations of anything beyond death have had these experiences. However, these people are convinced of some spiritual realm after such a momentous event in their lives.

As human beings we have a tendency to cling to the familiar and are fearful of the unknown. Sometimes we would prefer to cling to a fondly held misconception than open our minds to the possibilities of the unknown. I encourage people, when diagnosed with a life-threatening disease, to 'go for peace' rather than 'go for a cure'. Peace is absolutely achievable. We experience peace when we are affirming life in its fullness. We affirm life through our diet, our exercise, our treatment, our positive and uplifting thoughts and attitudes, through meditation and relaxation techniques, through forgiveness of past actions, through visualisation techniques, through the relinquishing of anger, guilt, blame and so on. This is not a laid-back, 'don't care' attitude. That is not peace. Peace is a dynamic state achieved through conscious choice. It is not resignation in the face of defeat, it is not a passive acceptance, but rather an attitude of maximising the possibilities for life in any given situation in a harmonious way. When we aim for this dynamic state of peace, we create the perfect environment for healing to take place. When we go all out for a cure, what we are really saying is that our healing has to be on our terms. With this thinking, if we don't succeed in curing our disease, we certainly won't experience peace either. There is a certain frenetic quality about people who are determined to cure the illness at all costs. The cost, inevitably, is our peace of mind. This attitude rather misses the point of healing. Health *is* inner peace. Certainly, most of us would rather remain in our bodies, with our loved ones, doing the things which are familiar and which we have always enjoyed. And yet, so many of us resist life — wanting it to be on our terms. Michael's experience of profound peace and openness to life in the midst of his parting, was a healing indeed. And his healing extended to touch the hearts of his family and those close to him and brought them comfort. To lose our 'clinging' to life is not giving up. It is more a giving over to life. It embodies a trust in the perfect unfolding of each moment — each moment full of potential, full of healing, full of peace.

Society equates 'success' with people living, and 'failure' with people dying. This is a totally wrong criterion. It is still common in hospitals to see curtains drawn around the 'dying patient' and for there to be an air of reluctance on the part of the nursing staff to enter. It has been shown that nurses take longer to answer the bell from patients who have been classified as 'terminal' than from their other patients. Most people feel uncomfortable in the presence of someone who is doing something *they* are frightened of doing.

When I was training as a nurse at the age of seventeen, I was struck by the strange ritual which seemed to surround the patients who were dying. The curtains were drawn and a nurse would occasionally tip-toe to the curtains, opening them to report back whether the patient was still breathing or not. Second hourly back rubs and turns were still performed but with the maximum speed possible in order to be relieved of the 'internal' discomfort clearly experienced by the nurse.

I was considered to be a bit 'weird' by the other nursing staff, because I really wanted to *be* with these people, and not relinquish care at a time when it was obvious that the presence of someone else could bring some measure of comfort. One patient, Mr Bradley, taught me much. He was an elderly man with the clearest blue eyes. He had a firm Christian faith and he told me he would welcome death because then he would be with Jesus. As his time drew close, the curtains were drawn, and he was left alone, I used to feel guilty whenever I slipped into his 'enclosure' in case the other nurses would talk about me — reinforcing my 'weird' reputation. Once behind the curtains, Mr Bradley and I entered another world. I would hold his hand and reassure him, maybe reading him something from his beloved Psalms. His face would soften and his body would relax. When some fear, uncertainty or pain would cloud his face, I would stroke his brow and talk to him about Jesus. Again he would soften and open. I spoke to him in whispers for fear of the other nurses overhearing our conversations. We prayed. I even sang the 23rd Psalm softly to him. He liked that a lot.

He finally surrendered into stillness, one hand on his beloved Bible, the other in mine. Although Mr Bradley was clinically dead, I could still feel his presence. There seemed to be a lightness, even a joy — certainly a feeling of expanded consciousness. I remained with him still talking quietly, unsure whether I was reassuring him or myself. It felt like an extraordinarily 'high' kind of experience and it took me some minutes before I was able to resume normal nursing duties. I was not permitted to wash his body as it was considered I had become 'far too involved already'. I believe it is a desirable quality for medical personnel who are working closely with people with life-threatening diseases that they are able to relate on an emotional level with their patients. This doesn't mean weeping all over them, though tears may certainly need to be shed. Professional colleagues need support groups just as the patients and their carers do.

Frequently in the busy-ness of diagnosis, treatment and never-ending tests, the patient as an individual can feel totally lost. One of the most dearly held qualities for any individual is that of dignity. This quality, more than any other, embodies the individuality of the person. A patient's reaction to all that is said or done to him will be filtered through his consciousness of dignity.

As a teenager, I spent many months confined to bed in hospital whilst undergoing reconstructive surgery on my legs. The agonies I experienced with bedpans are too awful to describe! For the first time in my life, I became severely constipated simply because I could not bear the lack of privacy my situation incurred. To the nurses, the fact there was a six-inch gap where the curtains didn't meet was unnoticed. To me, I felt the entire gaze of the world beaming in, not to mention the ears. So insurmountable a problem did it seem to me, I even took to throwing my food out of the window in the hope that if nothing went in, then it would be unnecessary for anything to come out. The agonies of personal vulnerability! This is not false modesty: it is a deeply held vulnerability which our dignity protects. The importance of respect for the dignity of the individual must remain of paramount importance. I well remember the frail hand of an elderly woman reaching down to retrieve the sheet which had left her nakedness exposed after she had been sponged.

Ultimately, it is the patient who must choose their doctor, their treatment and the way in which they will conduct their life, and we must accord complete respect to the individual and their choices. This can be quite difficult for both the family and the patient where there is disagreement over the continuation of any type of treatment. Oftentimes the patient has considered the options available and has decided to discontinue treatment, and yet the family will still be holding on to the hope of success through the continued implementation of treatment.

One lady, Pamela, had been undergoing treatment for three years. Each time she ceased a course of chemotherapy the secondary tumours in her lungs would reappear. Her overall health was alright though she was becoming increasingly depressed by the physical limitations caused by prolonged chemotherapy. The doctors had always told her the chemotherapy was only to keep her comfortable and there was no possibility of remission. Pam was also working a great deal with meditation and her philosophy about life had undergone quite significant changes during the time of her illness. She began to trust more deeply in herself and in God. She let go much of her clinging to life.

Her family, meanwhile, was very keen to have her continue treatment, at all costs, because it was the only way they believed she could stay alive. This view was yet another stress to Pamela.

She felt she lived in a limbo world — neither dead, nor fully alive — unable to participate in the activities of the family. She felt she was only observing life and that, in herself, she was at peace. Her peace was only disturbed when she tried to do things she was incapable of attaining, or when she wanted things to be different from the way they were.

It took a long discussion with her family, in which many tears were shed, and it was finally decided Pamela would cease her treatment. This occurred only after discussion with her doctor, who understood her viewpoint and accepted her decision. Once these discussions had taken place, the atmosphere seemed to change amongst the family members. A closeness developed in far more tangible ways than had been experienced before. Words of support and love were spoken rather than withheld. Family members made time available to reminisce with Pamela over the past. Photographs were brought out and memories relived. It takes courage to be open-hearted in the midst of personal pain and yet it is possible. Our lives can become enormously enriched by this process.

Practical Aspects

There are many aspects surrounding dying which you may wish to discuss at some time with your family or loved ones. Some people prefer to do this right near the time of diagnosis. It is not morbid to talk about your wishes and desires for the future. You will want to 'tidy things up' so that there is little unfinished business for your family to manage.

Part of this procedure would be the formalising of your will, if not already done. This is not a negative action, nor does it mean you are affirming death. Any lawyer will suggest this be done at a very early age. You may also wish to state certain preferences for the education of your children or even make tapes for them to play when they reach certain stages in their lives, or leave them something in writing.

One family, recognising that their beloved father, grandfather and great-grandfather was not long for this world, asked him if he would make a tape, detailing the family history. Eric felt deeply touched by their request and the family ended up with a dozen tapes of his reminiscing over his childhood; how their ancestors had emigrated to Australia; anecdotes of various family members; incidents, long-forgotten or never heard of by the family. Interwoven throughout these stories was the philosophy and essence of Eric. After his death, they had the tapes transcribed so each family had a copy of his memoirs.

When talking with your family, you might wish to give expression to any strongly held ideas you may have on how long life-support systems should be continued; how sedated you would like to be; say whether you would prefer to be at home or in hospital, and who you would like to have with you.

The majority of people prefer to remain at home to die. This used to be the accepted practice. To die comfortably at home requires good support from your loved ones. They also need to feel supported. One of the aspects of my work now is in training what I call 'midwives for the dying'. It is my belief that we need just as much assistance to leave this world as to enter it. These 'midwives' go beyond just the physical care of the patient. They work with massage, techniques of relaxation and visualisation, counselling children and family members, and generally facilitate in the situation so that everyone comes through the experience in as healthy a way as possible. It is no longer surprising to me to hear the family left behind say they felt a kind of 'rightness' and joy, as well as sadness, at the passing of their loved one. The chief role of the 'midwife' is to remain calm and at peace whilst being really open to the situation. When there is this feeling of calmness and competence the rest of the family, and indeed the patient, relax easily into each unfolding moment.

Be brave enough to face these practical questions so you know these details have been taken care of. In this way you will be free to enjoy your family, enjoy your relaxation and flow into the peace of mind which your meditation brings and allow it to play its full part. These discussions with the family are often difficult to get started but once underway they seem to flow along very easily. It is almost as if there is a release in being able to talk about an area of our lives which is potentially so painful.

My grandmother, for the last ten very full years of her life, made it her practice to put labels underneath all her possessions. This included everything from small Royal Worcester ornaments to large carved sideboards. These labels indicated who she wished to have these life-long treasures and it gave her pleasure to think of that person enjoying them. As a young child I often would peek under an ornament to see who it was 'going to' and in this way I felt quite at home, though a little awed, at the process of living in, and leaving this world.

I know many people who have orchestrated their funeral well before the event. They have chosen the music, and in some cases have prepared the readings or other content they wish included at the service. For example, it was a source of satisfaction to Brian, who was diagnosed with AIDS to choose what was to be done with his ashes and to completely arrange the service. He also talked to his partner about future relationships Steven might have and how he felt about them. He died very much as he lived: courageous and open to life.

Know that as you prepare for the physical fact of death that you will also experience yet another wonderful and positive aspect of life. We go through many emotions when we contemplate our own death. Elisabeth Kübler-Ross has done much to enlighten the community about this process. She classified five distinct stages through which all people pass who are dying. These stages do not come in any particular order. Often we hop from one stage to another within moments. It can be helpful to be aware of these stages so that when we experience them, we can know we are not alone in our experience. Many others have passed this way before. At the time when I was sick, I was unaware of this research and yet, looking back at my experience, I certainly passed through each of those stages. When I was actually in some of them, it was very hard to maintain any objectivity. I sometimes seemed to be quite engulfed by the emotions.

The stages that have been clearly identified are:

Denial

This stage may be quite prolonged or very short. The mind may simply scream an inward 'NO!' There was a part of me denying the diagnosis until real weakness set in. Some people who fall into the high-risk groups for infection with the HIV may well go through denial before they ever go to have a confirming blood test.

Anger

This is the classic 'Why didn't it happen to someone else? Why me?' As in denial, this stage may be very brief or prolonged, depending on the individual. I didn't go through the 'Why me?' so much as the frustration of feeling helpless against an unseen monster. I was angry because I felt out of control, unable to exert any influence over my bloodstream.

Bargaining

This one can be very complex. It can become the driving force behind our actions. 'If I drink carrot juice three times a day, eat all that healthy food, take my vitamins, exercise, meditate and relax then, my reward *should* be that I get well.' The people who embrace this philsophy are usually unsuccessful in achieving peace of mind. Many of us slide into this thinking periodically, especially when we have found a new lump, or our tests weren't too good. Our reaction can very easily be: 'But I've been doing everything right.' There is nothing wrong with doing all the above things in order to increase our level of health and well-being. It is the motivation behind those actions which becomes so important. The above thinking stems from the attitude 'If I'm good enough, maybe I'll make the grade'. Remember, many of us had a life of 'If I'm good enough . . .' so be wary of allowing it to colour your motivation. This can also extend to a renewed vigour in our church attendance: 'If I confess all my sins, if I pray regularly, if I attend church weekly, then maybe the Lord, in His infinite wisdom and mercy will let me get well.' It may well be that attendance at your church, or regular meditation, will bring you great peace of mind and that healing may take place. That's great! Your motivation was probably to re-establish your connection with God and your own inner peace and to cultivate the trust that all was unfolding just as it should. There is no reason why we can't have the preference of wanting to be healed! It is when we have an 'addiction' to being healed that problems arise: 'I can't have peace of mind *unless* I'm healed.'

I found I slipped in and out of this kind of bargaining. For me, it was the great issue of trust, of letting go of control. I found it difficult at times to do all the things to affirm life and then sit back and trust all was unfolding appropriately. Our motivation can be quite subtle.

Depression

This is a difficult time for both the patient and the family. The family or loved one may feel quite excluded from the emotional presence of the patient. They may feel very helpless. We tend to be more prone to depression when everything *isn't* going right. It may well result from some subtle influence of the bargaining attitude. 'I've been doing it all right — why aren't I getting better?' By resolving the issues which surface through our depression, we can make great grounds inside ourselves. In fact, I believe more healing can sometimes take place by working through the issues involved in depression, than when we are flying high and feeling fantastic. The depressions I experienced were abysmal, and yet I learned greatly from them.

Acceptance

Acceptance really embodies the trust that all is well. Even dying is alright. One mother, Vivien, had been working with her cancer for two years. She had two small boys and a devoted husband. Over those years, she frequently voiced her sadness and depression over the possibility of leaving her little children. We had talked of her spiritual beliefs often and these had deepened and expanded during that time. The week before she died, I visited her and we spoke again of her leaving the children. She said she felt completely assured that they would be alright without her and that her husband would also. She said she felt completely healed and well. Vivien spoke of great inner peace saying she felt part of her had 'gone' already. In her last days she took on a beautiful and translucent look. Her acceptance permeated the household. Her parents, husband and children were fully involved in her passing, and were open and in touch with their own emotions.

In addressing the fears and uncertainties of our own death, we also expose the fears and uncertainties present in our living. We do not need a life-threatening disease in order to look at the issues around our own death. When we embrace life fully, we are more ably equipped to relinquish our hold on a body which has served its purpose well. One of the greatest keys to living and to dying is the practice of meditation. Through this practice we begin to understand and experience our real and unlimited nature. With this experience comes a deep, unshakable peace and the certain knowledge that we are indeed far more than just our bodies. When we are firmly rooted in this knowledge, derived from experience, our reality becomes one of complete safety and trust, and we experience our true, indestructible nature.

Young Peter, all of four, summed up rather well after his mother, Vivien, had died. He peered into her eyes and said, 'Yep, she's definitely gone.' He looked up then and saw a picture of himself and his mother on the dresser. He ran and got it and said, 'This is how I remember Mummy. The light is in her eyes, but now it's gone.' Peter and I have had discussions since; he has asked simple questions like, 'How did the light leave her eyes?', 'How did she (her spirit) leave the house?', 'Did she go through doorways, out the window or could she go right through the wall?' His level of acceptance of the fact of his mother's death was absolute and his questions were those of the curious and the intelligent. It is good to have such questions. We talked about how, whenever he thinks of his mother, he can feel her soft warm presence in his heart.

Another little boy had a similar experience. I had sat with him by his mother's body. We had 'tuned in' to our hearts and had invited the lovely presence of his mother into them. Afterwards I had told him that any time he sat down quietly and thought of her, he would feel her presence in his heart. A few days later, after the funeral, Damien was running by, playing with some other children. He came over to me and said, 'You're wrong you know. I don't have to sit still to feel her in my heart. I can feel her there when I run too!'

Chapter Thirteen

Case Histories

Here are some characteristic, and very often very poignant, case histories, told from the immediacy of first-hand experience:

Kate

Our daughter was first diagnosed as having cancer in May 1984. We were devasted with the news and, a sort of numbness and disbelief came into our lives. Of course, we asked the question: Why our child? — so fit and healthy before this most dreaded of diseases appeared in her body. Her particular cancer, rhabdomyosarcoma, was in the left ventricle of her heart, so open-heart surgery for its removal was arranged as quickly as possible. Recovery from the operation, radiotherapy, and then two years of chemotherapy followed. Kate was almost six at the time of diagnosis, and it was all a very traumatic experience for her. I think of the times when we held her down to put the chemotherapy into her small veins, and I shiver. What have we put our child through? What have we done to her small body to try and rid it of this disease?

Overall, she coped really well and I think always telling her the truth about her disease and what was happening helped her to do that. When her two years of treatment was up we were so happy; now our family could return to normal and we could get on with our lives! Ten months after Kate came off treatment she relapsed with another tumour in the outer lining of the heart; this one was inoperable, being in the position it was, so more chemotherapy followed in an effort to shrink it. Six months later it began enlarging, so, radiation was advised. Kate had the maximum dose possible. We were offered more chemotherapy to keep her comfortable, and that was all that was left. To hear those words 'There's nothing more we can do for your child', is shattering. At the thought of having her away from home for one week out of four, and, with the sickness and trauma that would follow chemotherapy, we decided that if her time was to be short, then, we would rather have her at home where she was happiest. So we said no to more chemotherapy. We thought it was pointless when it had not done what it was supposed to earlier on. We came home in October 1987, severing our ties with traditional medicine and the hospital.

I can tell you we were one uptight family with the stress of the relapse; I think it is worse to deal with than at the time of initial diagnosis. What we initially had faith in — modern medicine — was not working for our child, but, no matter what the future held, we just wanted to be home where we could love and care for our child the best way we knew.

My husband, being provider and protector of the family, was filled with hopelessness and rage and found it very difficult to cope with the situation of being unable to help his child. The stress of the last three and a half years was catching up. My position was made easier by my Christian faith which gave me an inner peace and strength to cope. Not that it wasn't sorely tested from time to time.

We were frightened to start with, not knowing where to turn, so we started reading lots of books on alternative medicine, diet, other cancer patients' stories and so on. My husband looked to overseas as a possible option during the first weeks when panic set in, and he felt we had to continue with some form of treatment straight away, once we left the hospital. I know that fear and worry is our worst enemy, so I would pray a lot about things, and just hand the situation over to God. After extensive reading it appeared that there is nothing written specifically for children, which meant we had to choose what we thought appropriate, and what our child could handle without any additional stress.

After seeing several naturopaths, we chose one that had a warm caring nature, was full of compassion and understanding and who brought out in us a special feeling that all was not lost, and that the path we had chosen was the right one. We started altering Kate's diet to mainly raw food, or lightly steamed, with a little chicken and freshly caught fish, plus vegetable juices, plenty of fruit and some vitamin supplements. She does visualisation, and we have told her that her efforts in this and other areas is helping to create the ideal environment for healing. We can only do so much as parents with our love, support and guidance. It was not easy having to enforce on a child a strict eating pattern, but we felt that now Kate is nine and a half, she is old enough to understand what we are talking about, and she knows this is the best way for her. Seven months on, the quality of our life as a family is enriched by our decision; our daughter is happy, full of life, vitality and cheek, and, no matter what the future holds for us we know that every day is precious and that we have made the right choice.

If you are a parent in our situation, I encourage you to never, never give up hope. There is always something that can be done and if you look, the path will be opened to you. Life after cancer will never be the same for a family, regardless of the outcome, as all our emotions and feelings have taken such a battering. We have learned to appreciate one day at a time, we can still laugh, and a good cry comes easily. But hopefully through the experience we may be able to help someone else; we have certainly learned a lot ourselves.

With love,
Julie and Ray

Joyce

No-one told me this was going to happen. No-one told me I would get AIDS. No-one predicted: 'Joyce's days will be numbered when she turns 35.'

It's crazy. Good health runs in my family, at least for the women. I had always expected to live to some respectable old age, like 90, so I never rehearsed the role I'm playing now. It was forced on me almost a year ago when Dr Tattersalls came into my room at Sydney's Royal North Shore Hospital and told me my AIDS test was positive.

Talk about ignorant. I think my first words were, 'What does that mean?' Sue Tattersalls is not one to mince words. In her dry and unemotional English manner she said simply, 'You have Category A of the AIDS virus, in other words, you have AIDS.' Damn. I had admitted myself to hospital two days before with pneumonia. I figured it was an extended cold — a result of overstressing my system. Just a few days in hospital and I'd be out, continuing my life with a few good hospital stories to tell. AIDS was quite a surprise.

'How long have I got, Doc?' I just couldn't help myself. I'd watched this scene on television a thousand times and I had to ask. Her reply was somehow disappointing. 'We don't make any predictions with this virus — It's too variable.' A younger thoracic doctor stood motionless behind her. He had admitted me, so I looked to him for some sort of reasonable, sane comment like... 'Ha, ha, just kidding, wanted to see if you were paying attention.' He didn't. He looked scared. I kept looking into their eyes, hoping for a bolt of lightening to strike me dead. Time stopped. I stared at these two faces. What was I supposed to say? Shouldn't I be kicking and wailing, or screaming at the top of my lungs 'I want to live!' And why was everyone still so normal? *I have AIDS* and no one is reacting! *My life is being threatened.* Doesn't that mean absolutely anything to the rest of the world?

The doctors said I was in shock. Like hell I was. I just freaked out a little, that's all. I've never faced anything like this before, for Christ's sake.

I had to wait two hours for my housemate Andy to show up. As those 120 minutes ticked by, an exquisite nurse stood next to my bed and listened. I don't remember what I told her, but I'm sure it had a lot to do with that 'life flashing before your eyes' business. I probably rambled on and on about my family, my friends, my loves — you know, my whole existence. I guess I was trying to comprehend what the doctors had told me.

My mind was hammering questions. What does having AIDS mean? What's going to happen to me? Am I going to shrivel up and die like a cancer patient? Am I going to spend the rest of my life in and out of hospitals, constantly on some sort of drug? How long have I got? But no-one could give me any answers. I had heard the news reports: A lingering and horrid death. One or two years. Social rejection. A definite dampener on your social life.

After forever, Andy peered around the curtain, grinning from ear to ear. 'I think I've gotten everything you asked for. Here's something to add a little colour.' He laid the flowers on the side table and proceeded to place the other items on my bed . . .

chocolates, magazines, needlepoint, books. 'Andy, they've told me what I have.' He was so calm, so unsuspecting, just like me. 'I have AIDS.' Disbelief, amazement, intrigue. We just sat there, saying 'I don't believe it' over and over again. He held my hand and didn't shed a tear. I kept feeling myself floating away. Call it low blood gasses, shock, whatever, but I felt my soul leaving my body. I kept saying to Andy, 'Touch me. Touch me, I think I'm slipping away.' He brought me back and told me we were going to get through this thing. 'Don't worry, Joyce,' he said. So I didn't.

I spent three weeks in hospital, combating pneumocystic pneumonia (PCP). Only people with cancer and AIDS get this type of infection. The doctors told me later I was a very sick girl and could've died. Funny, I never thought I was that sick. In fact I thought PCP would be much more devastating than it was. Of course, the antibiotics I swallowed (and took by I/V drip) made me vomit *all* the time, but I got used to it. I actually could carry on an intelligent conversation with a green bowl tucked under my chin — I learned to be sick without missing a word!

I lost a lot of weight in hospital (but who's complaining?), cut my hair off to keep if from strangling me during the night, and had to learn to walk all over again — for almost two weeks I was too weak to walk at all. But, apart from the multitude of holes drilled into me by various-sized needles, I thought I was still the same old Joyce who had hobbled into the emergency room gasping for breath.

I was wrong. In those few weeks, my life changed more than it ever had before. But it took several more weeks before the new reality sunk in. While hospitalised, I had diverted my attentions away from the virus by being funny and sociable. The nurses loved me. But deep inside, I always knew when I went home the real battle would begin. I had a long, scary, but exciting, road ahead of me.

I never doubted my diagnosis. At least that moved me a step ahead in the Kubler-Ross stages of facing death. Acceptance, yes. How could I deny that I had AIDS? But I was still unsure on how long I had. I did know there would have to be drastic changes: in my diet, the way I think, who I spend time with, what I read ... my whole lifestyle, in fact.

My faith came to the rescue. A typical story, really. When things get really tough, the guy upstairs will *always* come through, and into my lap fell three little angels. The first was a social worker, Pam. The second, a doctor, Peter. The last, a nutritionist, Petrea. As a team they have done a lot more for me than their professional credentials may indicate.

Pam first visited me in the hospital the morning after my diagnosis. She visited me almost every day during my stay, talking about coping with my new self, answering questions about the nature of the HIV virus, and giving suggestions on how to tell my family and friends. Since I have a big family scattered all over the United States, I appointed one sister, Jennifer, to be the bearer of bad news. She handled the logistics and diplomacy beautifully, but I often think this whole mess is harder on the people close to me than it is on me. I think Pam was Mom. She was always there and she always listened and understood. She still does.

It's difficult to talk about Peter without breaking into a giggling, gushy 'He's sooo cute.' But he is. I first met Peter as he stood at the foot of my bed, a few days after my admittance. There were a gang of doctors, interns and nurses gathered around me. I was the first female, heterosexual, non-drug user, non-blood tranfusioned person with AIDS they had ever seen. They all talked amongst themselves and, as much as I wanted to join in, I was too weak and the oxygen mask made it even more difficult for me to be heard. My AIDS doctors, as I now referred to them, were asking the same old questions: How do you feel, Is your breathing better, Are you eating, Are you sleeping, blah, blah, blah. I was not listening. I kept staring at the foot of the bed wondering who the hell the hunk was. Without any warning, I turned away from the inquest, pulled off my mask, looked straight at Peter and said, 'My God, where did you come from. You are gorgeous!' The good doctor was embarrassed. Maybe this little incident started us off on the right foot. I now am closer to Peter than I ever thought was possible. He holds nothing back, and is honest about my physical condition. I think it's spiritual, past-lives and all that. Sometimes Peter thinks I'm nuts.

Through friends of friends, I learned of the Albion Street

Clinic — the headquarters for AIDS in Sydney. I was told that there was this woman, Petrea, who was working with gay guys and that she was really fantastic. She was also recommending a special diet, relaxation, meditation — the practices which I knew would benefit my condition. I made arrangements with her to meet me at my home, the day I was dismissed from hospital. She was very open and straightforward. 'She's got this down to a science,' I thought. 'She probably tells everyone the same line ... drink juices, give up cigarettes, no sugar, ask yourself if you want to live, and on and on and on.

Petrea is now my guru. She's taught me so much about living, how to regain quality in my life. She never promises quantity and she helps me understand death. When I went back into hospital for my second bout with PCP, she calmed me down before my bronchoscopy by massaging my toes. The trick worked. She has also agreed that if she is still alive when I die, she will take me to my death. That little promise is the most comforting thing I know.

So when people ask me, 'What do you do with your time?', I reply, 'I'm healing.' And it truly is just that. Every day of my life, I am healing myself in some way.

About six months after my diagnosis, I decided to take a holiday to see if I could survive without my three P's. I did, but I didn't like it. Until I get rid of this silly viral creature inside of me I want all the help I can get. It's a daily battle, living with AIDS. The situation doesn't suddenly change. I mean, you don't wake up one morning and not have AIDS. This disease will continue to threaten my life until a cure is discovered and I have a funny feeling it's going to take a lot longer than people are led to believe.

So, what do I look like? You think, 'Joyce has got AIDS!' and you see a frail, weak, hobbling invalid. Nope, not me. You're another victim of the sensational AIDS press, where pictures of emaciated vacant-eyed patients stare forlornly out of the glossy pages. Sorry. Maybe I'm the odd one out but I don't look like that. I've gained all (and I do mean *all*) my weight back. No gaunt, transparent looks from me. In fact, most of my friends are quick to comment, 'I don't know how to say this, Joyce, but you look better than you've looked for the last few years.' Thanks a lot. Just how bad *did* I look over the last few years, and why didn't any of you creeps tell me?

In sometimes bizarre ways, AIDS provides opportunities. As an example, one experience I thought I would never have was getting to know homosexuals. I was never particularly homophobic, but as an active heterosexual the thought of hanging out with men who loved men didn't sit right in my mind. However, shortly after I was diagnosed I began to attend a group therapy session at the AIDS Albion Street Clinic in Surry Hills. Once a week I was surrounded by gay men. The only other woman attending was the group's leader, my angel, Petrea.

Most of these guys were simply antibody positive — only a few had experienced their first opportunistic infection. They were a literate, sensitive, scared group of men and this was a very constructive experience. Take it from me, group therapy works. I felt secure and cared for with these guys. Only people with AIDS know what it's like to have AIDS. We exchanged countless hours of experiences, these boys and me. We talked about our families, our lovers, we wrestled with our living and dying, and prayed for those who suddenly departed, leaving us behind to continue the fight.

In retrospect, I've been lucky. I could have fallen ill in America. Americans are so paranoid; they've gone from the sublime to the ridiculous. Children who are infected have to go to court in order to attend school, restaurants are closed because the chef is gay, people's houses are burnt to the ground because a member of the family is AB-positive. Since being diagnosed, I've only lost a couple of friends, but they weren't close friends to begin with. Most of the people I socialise with find this virus fascinating. They're intelligent enough to know the facts about how the virus is transmitted and as long as I don't bleed on them or have sex with them, they're fine.

In fact, my friends and family have been 100 per cent supportive. They tell me I look good; they praise me for my strength; they crack jokes about AIDS and make me laugh. They learn from my experience. I suppose that's one positive thing about having AIDS. I can be a teacher, I can show my friends first-hand something they probably (hopefully) will never experience. I can demonstrate strength, perseverence, fortitude and most of all, a resolute respect for life. My situation is absolute proof of that old adage 'Don't put off 'til tomorrow'...

As we all know, there's no cure — yet. I tried AZT but it made me feel like I'd already died! Imagine the worst flu you've ever had in your life and multiply all those aches and pains by one thousand. No thanks! Quantity of life may be the answer for some, but give me good old quality any day. I'm sticking to my homeopathic approach, because it's working.

Sometimes I get so angry at the injustice of it all. Then I think about people who have cancer, multiple sclerosis or any other life-threatening disease and I realise my plight is not that much more severe. The most heartbreaking for me are the people with AIDS in jail. Imagine not having the freedom to come and go as you see fit in order to combat the virus. And then there are the children born with AIDS. It all seems so terribly unfair.

Finally, it really doesn't matter how long I've got. My life, or anyone's life for that matter, has to end sooner or later. When I wake up each morning, I thank God I'm alive. Then I try to accomplish as much as I physically can during the day — some days that's a lot, other days somewhat less. But I make each day count and I'm confident I will continue standing tall and strong against my temporary status of ill-health. At night, as I go to sleep, my conscience feels clear — I know in my heart I'm not letting anyone down: not myself, nor my family or friends, nor, for that matter, God. At the bottom line, I owe this to me. I owe this to my soul.

Joanne

My story begins on 2 May 1986 when at the age of 29 I gave birth to the most beautiful baby boy. My husband and I were ecstatic. This ecstasy was marred by the discovery the following day of a very obvious lump in my abdomen.

To cut a long story short, the next day a physician was called in and ten days later I underwent an 8½-hour operation to remove a primary cancer in my sigmoid colon and secondaries in my liver. I was left with part of my bowel removed, 75 per cent of my liver gone, no gall bladder and a less than 25 per cent chance of surviving five years.

I couldn't say I was devasted, as I was still thinking about my beautiful baby. It was more like a cruel blow and I just could not entertain the thought of dying. This was also due to the fact that my mother had bowel cancer four years previously (although she had no secondaries) and has survived, and also the wonderful memory of an aunt who had previously been given six months to live with cancer of the uterus which had spread extensively. The doctors thought she should stay in hospital until she died. She had a lot of reasons to live, so she jumped out of her bed and went cherrypicking in South Australia. She came back six months later and the doctors could find no evidence of cancer. She lived another 25 years and died at the age of 74 with bowel cancer, but this time she didn't want to fight. Her children had families of their own and her much-loved husband had died 18 months earlier. She was brave enough to make a conscious decision to die, just as she had earlier made a conscious decision to live.

With my aunt as an example I just assumed I could be one who lived too. So, for six months I made no changes to my life. Six months after surgery I had a scan and felt great apprehension on going to see my liver surgeon. He is a lovely man and as he put my scans on the wall I could see his chin trembling. He couldn't look at me as he told me as gently as he could that the cancer was back in the liver and had spread to the lungs.

I couldn't believe what I was hearing, I was devasted. I wanted to cry and scream but couldn't because I thought my surgeon would cry too, and I knew he was trying to keep his 'professional' composure. I wanted him to hold me but I wasn't game enough to approach him so I hugged my baby instead.

I went home and in my husband's arms we cried and cried. We discussed chemotherapy and decided to give it a go as there was a 10-20 per cent chance of going into remission, if only for a few months. There was no cure. I really felt as though I was looking down the barrel of a shotgun. I was actually faced with death.

My husband had decided he was going to find out everything he could about cancer and he contacted every organisation he could find to get information. As luck/or fate would have it I was desperate for Nigel to have a colonoscopy to make sure he didn't have bowel cancer and so he went to his general practitioner. My story was told and the doctor insisted I should see Petrea King.

Through seeing Petrea my whole world expanded amazingly. She was able to make me see that just because the doctors at Sydney's Royal North Shore Hospital had never seen anyone survive my type of cancer that there was no reason why I couldn't be the first one. At last there was hope!

I could see that I didn't have to give in to cancer. I could live with it and do things for myself instead of having things done to me all the time. I didn't have to be a victim.

So with great gusto I enthusiastically embraced meditation, vegetable juices, vitamins, minerals and a new diet. The greatest thing I discovered was that it would be a terrible tragedy if I died and the people closest to me did not know the *real* me. It took great courage to gather my family together and tell them about all the unresolved problems I had hidden inside me for the last 15 years. These problems were of mammoth proportions to me and when I told them these deep dark truths they were astounded — but guess what — they still loved me!

Oh, what a relief and what a great release. All my burdens were suddenly lifted from my shoulders. I felt free at last to be the real me...

In January 1987 I had an X-ray and the cancer had got worse. In Petrea's support group there was a girl whose brain tumour had got worse before it got better so this taught me that cancers could be turned around. I guess I was impatient for results.

We started getting newsletters from the Australian Cancer Patients Foundation and received great inspiration from the stories of people with medically 'terminal' cancers that are now totally free of cancer — it could be done. We went to Ian Gawler's Seven-day retreat near Melbourne and found this enlightening. I was committed to improving my lifestyle. After a holiday in New Zealand in February-March 1987 I returned to have a scan. The cancer had regressed amazingly and by July scans were showing I had no cancer at all. We were elated.

However, two months later the cancer re-appeared. I felt incredibly deflated. I soon realised that during the time that I appeared not to have cancer I was always wondering 'When was the bubble going to burst?' I wondered if all I had done was really worth it if in the end I couldn't shake off the cancer.

Then came another relevation. Of course it was worth it — the quality of my life had been better than ever since cancer.

I do not know if I am going to live a couple of months or until I am 100 but I do know that thanks to my family, my husband, Petrea, and the support group, my life has been immeasurably happier and exciting. I have just taken responsibility for my cancer and 'live' each day instead of just 'existing'.

I am the longest survivor of my type of cancer at Royal North Shore Hospital and the doctors don't know why I am still alive. Who *can* know?

All I know is that I love life and am no longer afraid of death and feel great about the future, no matter what happens!

Timothy

There is life after diagnosis. You have to take a little more care, but life goes on. I was diagnosed by a private doctor. The day my results were due, I had a morning appointment. The results hadn't arrived when I rang.

I was angry. I didn't want to go one more day without knowing; I wanted to know whether to throw a party or a wake!

The doctor said he wasn't supposed to ring through the result, but I told him I wasn't coming back to his rooms as I had a busy day. An hour later he rang me at work — it was about lunchtime. I had someone with me, someone waiting for me, someone on the other line. He gave me the news while all these people were around. I was HIV positive.

I had to act like he was telling me a delivery would be late. I couldn't be self-indulgent. I certainly couldn't burst into tears or panic in front of all the people around me.

I thanked him for phoning me, dealt with the people, and with the other phone call. Then I rang the Albion Street AIDS Clinic for the first time. I didn't see it as a death sentence. Before the official diagnosis I saw a negative or positive result being a death sentence. But when it was announced I was HIV-positive, I no longer saw it this way. I wanted to survive.

My instinct went from the black wall of anxiety to trying to break that wall down. That was my immediate concern because I had far too much to live for.

I thought the only obvious place to go was the Clinic because they could at least point me in the directions I needed to go. After a complete medical check-up and more blood tests — the results from my doctor didn't indicate T-cell counts or anything like that — it was just a straight, 'You got it'. I saw a counsellor and started trying to get some sort of plan of action worked out. I wanted to know what to do, how to do it, when to do it, and who to do it with.

I was aware of alternative medicines which were working in this area. I was aware of lots of things that were being done and I felt I needed to be immediately involved with them. I sat down with the counsellor and started putting it all down on paper — who I was, what was in my world, what had to be dealt with. The things which emerged were my marriage, my new babe, my other children, my business, my whole life.

All those things had to be dealt with very quickly for obvious physical reasons. The baby was three weeks old so my wife had to be told because she had to be tested.

What we had to do in that first session, and I had daily sessions after that for the first week, was work out how to break the news to my wife. I was diagnosed on a Wednesday and my plan was to tell her on Saturday. I needed a couple of days to get my package back together. My head was shooting off in all directions. There were a million and one questions I needed answered. I had to get myself back into an upright position. The Clinic advised me to leave telling my wife for a couple of weeks to ensure my strength. I would need even greater strength once the news had been broken, to help her cope. It would have been foolish for both of us to fall apart.

But, because there was a baby involved which could be antibody positive as well, it was absolutely vital that she was told immediately. The first few days were spent just on me: getting me organised. There was a lot of emotion, a lot of soul-searching. My first reaction was that I had let the side down, then 'Why me?' I kept trying to remember who could have done this to me — not for vengeance but just to pinpoint where it had come from.

The more I did that, the more I realised it was a complete waste of time. Like trying to find out where you picked up a cold. The fact doesn't change that you have the cold.

It was decided finally on the Friday that I would have to break the news the following day. Our marriage and our life were so incredibly happy at this time. Our baby was the first we had been able to have naturally. We had to go through intensive sub-fertile therapy to be able to produce our first two children. It took four years for each of them to come along. Suddenly, within six months of the second baby being born, my wife was pregnant again. This was such a tremendous boost. It was an incredibly happy period. I wanted to keep that Friday night and that Saturday morning free because for me it was the last happy period, the last truly happy, untainted period that I would ever see in my life again.

I set myself a time — midday. I got the children out of the house and prepared myself to tell her.

It was in the dining room. We sat down and I told her. I told her I had some very sad news — 'I'm HIV-positive.' There was no way I could beat around the bush.

A cloud came down over her. She sat there for an hour without saying a word, absorbing it. There wasn't much I could say. I wanted to tell her all the practical things that had to be done but I had just told a woman who had lived with me for fifteen years that those years weren't all they had been cracked up to be.

After that hour she talked to me a little bit about it. Her reaction? 'Lies, it was all lies. My whole life was a lie.' She felt I had seen her as a substitute male. She doesn't understand the subtleties of bisexuality and we are still working on that one a year down the track. Then she asked me to go out. When I came back later that day, she told me she had spoken to her family. Then it was nothing else for the rest of that day until she asked me to go out again.

I picked up the children, had dinner with my sister who knew, and arrived home around midnight. I was promptly ushered to the couch. That was where I was sleeping and probably would be forever. I took up my position on the couch and hoped for better things tomorrow.

The next day, the Grim Reaper started coming in with an

advertising campaign.* My wife's reaction? 'I hope you die, because you deserve it', or comments like that. There was a lot of anger, a lot of terror, a lot of tears, a lot of accusation.

Then it was silence. Any communication was vicious and angry. It was all I could expect.

But the practicalities had to be taken care of. She had to be tested.

On the Monday I set up the appointment. It was Easter week and we had to have the results before the four-day holiday weekend. Why wait? It was a horrifying day for all of us.

Late in the afternoon, I had a phone call. 'Mum's arrived.' These were our conversations. Only the necessary words. Then the phone was banged down.

That completely threw me. I felt confident I could deal with things while there were no outside interference. Suddenly mother was on the doorstep with return tickets for my wife and children.

I was trying to keep myself together. From the outset, I wanted the end-result to be that my life would be intact and not in tatters. Immediately, I rang the Albion Street Clinic. It was my umbilical cord. I had to have someone to cry on but not one that cried too.

I fell apart. My wife's mother had flown in with only one mission — to get the family onto the next flight. I had to prevent that from happening.

At this stage, I was still terribly guilty. I didn't want to be kicked but I knew I deserved to be. All that has gone now. I no longer feel guilty. But this was only three days after being told I was HIV positive. I spent two hours at Albion Street working out how to deal with it. The only way was for me to operate from a position of strength. I couldn't let the family see any cracks. They would have ripped me to shreds. So, I greeted my mother-in-law with open arms and thanked her for coming, because we needed her. But I was still on my own — there was no communication.

The results of my wife's test were due on Holy Thursday. I knew she was getting them in the afternoon and she had said she

* *This is a reference to a recent Australian television advertisement, warning of the grim consequences of AIDS — editor.*

would ring. I knew if she was antibody positive it would be the last words we ever said to each other.

She phoned. She was negative. Down went the receiver.

It was as if ten tonnes had been lifted from me. That left just me with the problem, and that changed the rules completely.

There was a lot of fear in me, the fear of God. One half of me said I was going to die tomorrow but the other said that this fat, forty-year old had no intentions of dying.

I had to go back to base, back to religion, to score some brownie points. I made a bee-line for the parish priest. I was trying to smooth the way to heaven. I did the whole reconciliation number.

On Easter Friday I gathered up the family and we all went off to mass. That night, I went to a Gay Catholic mass. It was full-on for me for three or four weeks. I was going to become the Pope if I was around long enough.

Of course, my wife's comment was, 'He's now gone completely loopy. He's now taken to religion.'

When my mother-in-law flew out a few days later — I had spent no time with her — she made the point that my wife still had the airline tickets for herself and the children. She was saying that if I messed up again they were on their way. The attitude was that I had been a bad boy and I had been caught. If I was a bad boy again ...

Now, I had to start rebuilding my marriage, my business, my life. The first couple of months was the heavy shock period. I couldn't do a lot to help myself. I was just running around.

You can't be told you're not going to die next week. There is hysteria. There is panic. I even went to an astrologer to see if I should make future plans.

I had every symptom. It was crazy. I rang my sister at three a.m. one morning because I was sweating. She just asked how much I had been drinking. There is always a logical explanation.

Then, one day I looked at my diary for the week and there were more AIDS related meetings than business ones. That was ridiculous. I was spending about ten hours a week at AIDS meetings. It was overkill. My whole existence was focused on AIDS.

Through Albion Street Clinic I was put in touch with Petrea

King. She changed my diet, put me on supplements, meditation, relaxation and visualisation.

I started doing exercise. I tried to cut back on alcohol and cigarettes. I'm still having a hard time with that. I enjoy both and don't see the point in throwing it all away. But I'm maintaining very good health, so something is on my side.

Petrea is the only weekly appointment I still have. The others have dropped off, apart from three-monthly check-ups at the Clinic. As my ability to cope has increased, my need for outside support has decreased.

It's a lot of fun...now. I'm enjoying it, not necessarily beating AIDS or winning over it — I don't think anyone can — but controlling it. My visualisation is that it's lurking in my big toe and is too scared to come out because it will face such a fight. As long as I keep that in my mind, it stays there. If I lose that image for a minute, then I panic.

At the beginning, if I cut myself I panicked in case someone touched my blood. At my first party I clutched my glass as if it were on fire. Living with an HIV-positive patient is simple common sense — you don't share toothbrushes, you don't share razors, you don't share needles. There's no drama.

We've gone past all that hysteria now.

The one thing that has pulled it off for me is that I have been able to laugh at myself, and *it*. When I started putting on weight I thought, 'This is ridiculous. I'm the only HIV patient in the world who is putting *on* weight.'

My wife is still angry. She still wants to have a go. But, she still loves me. And trust is returning.

We are sleeping together again. The irony is when we are making love, she doesn't want me to put the condom on. It's then that I want to say, you must understand how it happened to me.

Here we have a highly intelligent woman who knows the risks but suddenly she is lying in bed naked with someone she loves. You have to make yourself think rationally.

It's hard work. There are times when I want to be cuddled, when I need someone to say it's O.K., your're doing fine. But I have to do that for my wife. I'm her partner and I have to support her. She is doing that for me in her own subtle ways.

Sometimes we talk rationally about what has happened but it

always comes back to 'Why?' The question I want answered is not 'Why?' But 'What now?' That's more positive.

We had to decide if we were going to save our marriage and family. But my wife was the only one who could come up with the answer. It was up to her. She has said that if she finds out I have been with another man, it's finished. I don't know how long we can live like that. But I'll sort that out when I get to it. Hopefully, by then, she won't see me as a two-headed monster.

I have always been bisexual. So why married? Social pressure — and I loved her. The attitude to marriage has changed a lot in the past twenty years. I was caught up in that 'sixties thing: boy meets girl and it simply had to happen. You couldn't stay single.

You have to work at relationships, whether you settle down with a man or woman. I'm not a 'relationship hopper'. I don't think you walk out when things get tough. The problems are not going to change because of a change in partner.

When you find someone reasonably compatible, you may as well kick it along for the rest of your life. I don't want to do it alone. In some strange and silly way, I'm happy it all happened. I never considered lying because I wanted it all out. I thought, no more lies. I'm happy in myself. I don't believe I carry this cloud of death around me. I think if it had to happen to anybody, I'm glad it happened to me. A lot of people wouldn't have been able to deal with it as well. The thing that worries me is that there is not enough work being done out there in the community.

When the AIDS epidemic first hit, I started taking precautions immediately. I know in the gay community there are still people living on the edge with no protection.

Where do I go from here? Onwards — I get on with my life. You don't give up living because you are HIV-positive. You still have to be a participant in the world.

You think about it like you think about other things in your life. As you go through the day you think about your partner; what you are having for dinner; is the car going to start; I have to do this; I have to do that; I'm antibody positive; how's the bank balance today? It becomes part of life. You can't get out of bed every morning worrying about what is going to happen.

I have a very busy, happy home life. I enjoy being there. I don't resent my marriage. I don't resent my children. I'm not trapped. There's only one thing that's going to keep me healthy and that's me.

My bisexuality is going to be a problem in the future. It's not going to go away. But I'm still a nice person. I still like me. I have no regrets. I look at my life and I wouldn't change a thing.

Pamela

I first went to Petrea's support group in January 1987. Two months earlier I had been diagnosed as having chronic myeloid leukaemia. I was receiving medical treatment, but I was well aware there were many measures I could take to complement orthodox therapy. A friend in Canada had breast cancer a few years ago, and I knew she had taken control of her illness and adopted complementary therapies such as meditation. She remains absolutely sure they were responsible for her recovery. My husband and I had also attended a National Cancer Patients Foundation residential course run by Ian Gawler.

Despite all of this I turned up to the group with a fair amount of trepidation, having no idea what to expect and little idea of what I wanted. Within a few minutes I realised this group was dealing very honestly with matters that were important to them. People were talking about how they felt. As at Ian Gawler's, people who were 'medically' very ill, looked and sounded so very different from my previous, stereo-typed view of cancer patients. I felt this was the sort of group I wanted to be part of, because of the way people were able to discuss their feelings about the particular problems that beset them. For example, some members were discussing the emotional problems or solutions to such problems, attached to their Christmas celebrations, instead of merely recounting what they had done or where they had been. I decided that day I would attend as often as possible, given that I live four hours drive from where the group is held.

The group makes me realise my problems are often similar to those of others and that I am not alone. The group focuses on one person's problems and helps them find their own solutions. This process always sheds light on something that has been worrying me, even if I had not previously realised this. For example, many members have great problems in putting themselves and their needs first. This is essential for the whole approach because, if you do not, those helping you cannot either. It is not selfish, it is just commonsense — you can't help others without fulfilling yourself. Much of the discussion focusing on other people has been useful for me in learning how to articulate my needs to other people and in learning how to put myself first when necessary.

One perception the group and Petrea have assisted me to achieve is the realisation that if I die 'young' or from my cancer, it will not be because I have failed, or because the approach I am taking has failed. It will be because that was my time to die. I don't want to die yet and I have every intention to live as long as possible but I am no longer afraid of being a failure if I do die. Meanwhile I try to love and live every day. This is difficult for me because I always thought I would have fun in the future, but never quite got beyond the present chores. Everything I did was a chore — and I did the chore because I felt I 'should'. Now I try to think 'could' rather than 'should'.

Petrea and the group have filled the social space created by my leaving work. A lot of my stimulation had come from work and involvement with women's groups. The members of the support group feel like very real friends, even though I may only see them occasionally. We are always anxious to hear how the other members are. We share recent experiences, such as encounters with dispassionate doctors, which are easily understood and empathised with. Empathy *never* spills over into pity — a small but crucial distinction which I feel the group makes.

By contrast, it takes much work with some old friends to persuade them that I do not expect to die immediately and that while I am alive I want to carry on as normal a relationship as possible.

The group has greatly helped me confront many very negative emotions I have held about myself. To be welcomed with open arms, a big smile and the heartfelt remarks, 'How wonderful to see you' and so on, are in themselves so very self-affirming. For someone who has always thought themselves fairly useless and been surprised and disbelieving if people showed any evidence of thinking I was worthy of attention, the genuine respect shown to myself is wonderful. Somehow one feels very special, and worthy of love and of loving.

David

At 11 I became a practising homosexual.
At 15 a practising alcoholic.
At 24 a married bisexual and father.
At 26 I developed cirrhosis of the liver.
At 31 I became a sober alcoholic and a single homosexual.
At 36 I became a practising drug addict using marijuana, LSD, speed, cocaine, valium, sleeping tablets, cough mixture and antihistamines.
At 37 I became antibody positive to the AIDS virus.
At 38 my lover, Lee, died from AIDS.
At 39 I became a recovering alcoholic and addict.

I have been in this body for 40 years on 14 March 1988. When I was diagnosed as being antibody positive to the AIDS virus I retreated into drugs for a while to suppress the confusion and fear of having yet another life-threatening disease. After three months I decided to see how other people were coping with this AIDS thing and I joined a support group for people just diagnosed.

Around the same time I met some natural therapists who were advocating that diet, meditation and regular exercise were beneficial to the immune system. I decided I didn't need all that yet.

However, a month later my lover, Lee, was diagnosed with (AIDS-related) meningitis. I decided to give the relaxation and meditation a go. I joined a group and was pleasantly surprised to find that the classes provided me with the only peace in my week.

Several months later, upon his discharge from hospital, I became Lee's primary carer. At that time also I went away on a weekend seminar devoted to educating antibody positive people about nutrition, exercise and meditation.

About a month later, at a training group for AIDS support people, I saw Petrea for the first time and was intrigued by her personal health treatment of leukaemia. I enjoyed her relaxation and meditation technique so I joined her Thursday group at the the AIDS Clinic. Shortly after I consulted her privately about diet and vitamins.

A change in lifestyle was beginning.

I began taking vegetable juices, vitamins and minerals and changed my diet, avoiding red meats and dairy products, fats and oils and all processed foods.

I was still taking some drugs. Lee's condition was deteriorating and I was getting less and less sleep as he needed more and more of my time. Lee died on 27 January 1987.

My fighter T4 blood cells were quite good when I was first diagnosed, however, the ratio between them and the T8 cells was very poor. In February 1986 my T4s had halved in number. In May, after my first three months of meditation — also mostly drug free — these same cells had risen dramatically to high up in the normal range, and the ratio between them and the T8s was normal. They fluctuated again, due to the stress of Lee's illness and subsequent death. Since that time I have again instituted a healthy regime and, at present, after being drug-free for five months my T-cells are in normal range and their ratio is healthy.

I was fortunate to meet a doctor who gave me some very good advice. He said it was the patient's responsibility to adjust their lifestyle to one which was conducive to health by including nutritious foods, vitamins, exercise, positive attitudes, relaxation and meditation techniques.

For my alcoholism and addiction recovery I seek the support of associated recovery fellowships. They provide a programme of drug and alcohol-free living and the people with those groups have become my mentors and friends.

For my mental recovery after Lee's death and my reactions to being an HIV-positive homosexual, I have sought the support of a psychologist and attend a support group which he runs. And for my physical and spiritual recovery I have sought the guidance of Petrea King, who has not only shown me I can enjoy a healthy life but that my life can be filled with faith, hope and love.

These are my support network, plus all the AIDS-related

people who are such a powerful example of how to live and die with a quality of life previously unknown to me — plus my Mum and Dad.

My spiritual outreach has as much variety as the universe can supply. And I have learned that life continues after my bodily death and I will continue to learn even then.

Through safer sex comes self-respect. My joy and energy comes from caring, sharing and loving others.

Gay

I had always dreaded having cancer. As a fully fledged hypochondriac, I had worried for years about various parts of my anatomy. A tiny patch of flaky skin on my wrist was removable but able to cause undue panic. But somehow I had never considered breast cancer.

I had read a lot of the books. The Simontons on visualisation, Norman Cousins on laughing himself well. Ian Gawler's *'You Can Conquer Cancer'* made a great impression. At least, I thought, I knew what I would do. Meditation, visualisation, diet. Especially meditation.

I'd heard of Professor Christopher Magarey's theories about meditation and cancer. I'd been planning for years to learn to meditate — when I found the form that was right for me, when I found the right teacher, when... I had no doubts about its value and was always suggesting to my friends that *they* should do it.

Some years previously we had changed our diet — gone totally vegetarian. However, this had proved too strict and we had reverted to a diet which was mostly vegetarian, but supplemented by chicken and fish. It also included minimal dairy products, fats and sugar. We were also taking vitamin and mineral supplements, including Vitamin C.

When my mother developed lung cancer we suggested that she go with my husband and I to Dr Magarey's introductory meditation session at a Siddha Yoga Ashram. The chanting, incense and pictures of the Guru were all too much for a conservative elderly lady. Somewhat to our surprise, though, we loved it. Especially the chanting, which engendered a feeling of great peace and relaxation, a desire for it to go on and on. At about this time I began oestrogen therapy — oestrogen alone, and not combined with progesterone. I also reread Ian Gawler and can still remember feeling a strong conviction that, if I developed cancer, I would be able to 'cope', whatever that means. One can only reflect with amazement!

Then I discovered the lump. By chance, as I didn't regularly examine my breasts. I was shocked beyond belief. I didn't race off to the doctor. I thought I must have made a mistake, or at least that it would go away in a week or two. It didn't. I plucked up courage to make an appointment to see my gynaecologist and found she had gone on holiday over Christmas for three weeks. I decided I wasn't going to anyone else and told no one, not even my husband. I didn't realise gynaecologists only work below the waist! However I did stop taking the oestrogen.

I must have been her first patient after the holidays. She found the lump, which was very painful, and a mammogram confirmed its existence. It had not been there twelve months earlier. She recommended, and arranged, an appointment with a surgeon and in a week I was in hospital for a biopsy and the results. 'Bad news I'm afraid'. It seems incredible but I didn't even ask for a second opinion. Two days later I had a mastectomy.

Waiting for the results was nerve-wracking. (This feeling persists at check-up time, but lessens as time goes on.) The relief of finding that it had not spread to the bones, and then that the glands were also not involved somehow enabled me to cope with the operation. And to an extent one is in a state of shock. My husband was always there, solid as a rock, bringing fresh orange juice spiked with Vitamin C.

The knowledge that there was a network of friends thinking of and meditating for me, was tremendously supportive. I felt somehow surrounded by a cocoon of goodwill and love. Knowing that my mother-in-law lived for many years and my sister-in-law was alive and well over twenty years after each having had mastectomies gave me confidence that this wasn't necessarily the end of the line.

So I nagged to be let out of hospital. A friend, who thought stress was my problem, had suggested a special person who was very good with meditation and visualisation. Having already experienced a little of the Siddha Yoga we did not have to think about where to start and on the first visit recognised a mutual friend, also with cancer. She happened to mention that the highlight of her week was a support group led by a person with great understanding and insight. Instinctively I knew who it was going to be and that I must go. I made an appointment with Petrea King.

By this time post-operative confidence was turning to uncertainty, nagging doubt and paralysing fear of cancer in my remaining breast. From the first phone contact I'd felt an instant rapport with Petrea. My visits were tearful sessions. I thought I must be the only person to be so stupid, but found out I was just one of the club. Petrea knew all about us — the ones who presented a competent facade to the world but felt inside that we hadn't been around when the How To Do It Manual on Life was handed out.

Just after my first visit to Petrea, Ian Gawler had come up from Melbourne to organise a live-in workshop on Circular Breathing, a technique he felt was valuable in release of emotions without dramatic catharsis. I felt I should go, and some of the support group would be there. It was awful. However I didn't know how important it was going to be for me.

At an early morning meditation session Ian led a meditation, described in his more recent book *Peace of Mind*, in which he instructed us to focus on and visualise an area of concern — its shape, size, density etc. I decided to focus on my fear of cancer in the other breast. We were then instructed to breathe deeply into the area we were working on. Then the miracle happened. I can no longer remember what my fear 'looked like', except that it was grey. When I breathed deeply it shattered into a thousand tiny pieces and disappeared. I was released.

At the support group each week, I felt shy and reticent, and the tears annoyingly escaped, but no-one minded. On the second visit I was chosen for a 'hands on' healing. I longed for this touching but at the same time dreaded it because I knew it would start the tears rolling again. Tears had never been far from the surface — anger, sadness, laughter, rage — all could start the embarrassing waterworks. By now I was convinced that I would not be well until I had cried out the well of tears deep inside.

Sharing of feelings and problems in the support group is, at time, uproariously funny, constructive and practical (eg. how to deal with imposing families and friends trying to run our lives) and exciting (when someone has good results). It can also be confronting and at times is like looking down the barrel of the future — or at what it may hold. Mostly I feel I have received much more than I can offer in the support group situation.

Petrea's weekly meditation classes are addictive. Deep physical relaxation, followed by visualisation and meditation, produce a delicious state of being one wants to be in permanently. Practice at home is helped by a personal tape. Why then is it so easy to break the habit?

Drawings and their interpretation, as an insight into one's emotions, can be surprisingly revealing. Affirmations, setting goals and further reading (eg. Louise Hay's *You Can Heal Your Life*, and Lawrence Le Shan's *You Can Fight For Your Life*) have also been very helpful and stimulating for me.

Some people with cancer move from therapist to therapist trying out all sorts of different approaches. Sometimes I wonder: am I missing out on something I should be doing? For me, the one-to-one interaction with a support person is the most important requirement for change. The degree of confidence, trust and rapport in the individual are of great importance. For me, working with Petrea seems the right place to be. I'm lucky to have found that at the first try. I am now much more relaxed and comfortable with myself, as if the inner and outer selves are more in alignment. I am more able to let others be and am learning to say 'no' and not to worry about it. Peace of mind gradually develops — it is not an instant thing.

Change is not easy. Knowing that there is friendship, and support if one needs it, gives great strength.

Graham

AIDS. I still find that the word manages to stir up feelings of doom and gloom.

I guess that I first became aware of AIDS when reports of the American 'Gay Plague' started appearing in the Sydney Press. I remember thinking that it sounded horrific and I hoped that it would never come to Australia. One thing that I knew for certain, however, was that if it did come to Australia, I'd be all right because I wasn't as promiscuous as a lot of other people I knew. Besides, things like that only happened to *other* people.

I still don't know what finally prompted me to go and have that test. That whole part of my life now seems to be just a big blur. Actually I had been thinking of having the test for some time, to prove to myself that I was all right. The final catalyst came from an unexpected source. My 'friend' — if that's what you call the man with whom you've chosen to spend thirteen years of your life — and I went to see the play *As Is* with two friends. The play is about a relationship between two people, one of whom develops AIDS. It would be something of an understatement to suggest that we were all moved by it.

The next day I rang the Albion Street AIDS Clinic for an appointment for a test. The two-week wait seemed like a lifetime. The nurse and the counsellor who I saw asked me what I thought the result would be. Quite confidently I answered that I'd be HIV-negative.

I returned a fortnight later to be told that I was positive. How fortunate I was to have the benefit of a wonderful, compassionate doctor who broke the news to me, and a remarkable counsellor who spent some time with me as the reality of the news started to sink in. With enormous generosity these two continued to offer wonderful support through those very difficult early weeks.

Who could I tell? The first person whom I wanted to tell was my partner. In spite of the fact that we love each other dearly I was worried about how he would react to the news. I dreaded being greeted with anger or blame. It still amazes me how you can live with someone for thirteen years and still underestimate them so. However, he was just one of many people that I underestimated. He held me in his arms, told me how much he loved me and said that we would face this together. Together we planned who we would tell, and as the situation arose I told a few close friends.

I've often thought since just how fortunate I am. Most people sail through life never knowing how strong their friendships are. My God, I certainly found out very quickly. The friends I told were certainly saddened by the news, yet they all said the same thing: they loved me and would continue to love me. I'm embarrassed now to remember how much I underestimated them. I really think that I expected them to run away screaming, scared of catching the disease from me. Instead, they just came to me with outstretched arms, and they've all been there ever since.

My closest friends have a young child. For a time I attempted to avoid the child for fear of infecting him. (This was not a time of rational thinking for me!) They responded by literally picking him up and placing him in my arms. I regularly thank God for giving me friends such as these.

Deciding to tell my family was a little more difficult. Even though we are close, we had never really spent a lot of time discussing my sexuality. Once again they only offered a lot of non-judgmental support.

Very soon after, I found out that I was antibody-positive to the AIDS virus, I also found that I had Thrombocytopenia, a blood disorder causing me to bleed and bruise very easily. Coping with this soon became my major task in life.

All my life I seem to have felt the need to project an image of myself as a strong person, very much in control. One day, while I was out walking, I had a 'blinding flash' of realisation. It just came to me that I didn't have to cope and that it was all right for me to be upset, or angry, or frightened or whatever feeling I seemed to be experiencing at the time. This may seem somewhat obvious, but it changed my whole life. It actually gave me permission to feel in a way that I don't really think I had ever done before.

Around this time I became involved with various support groups. There were groups for people specifically with the AIDS virus and other groups for people with any life-threatening conditions. Once again I realise just how fortunate I was to be involved with so many compassionate and gifted people. This included those talented people facilitating and those attending the groups. It is so heartening to feel free to discuss any issues which I am facing, without any fear of being judged. Instead we seem to be linked by a common element of wanting to understand ourselves better and how we can help to create a healing environment in our bodies.

Attending these groups became almost a full-time job, and yet there seemed so many issues that needed to be resolved before I could get on with living. The major issue for me seemed to be that I had lost control of my life. I had an image of myself in a car, without brakes or steering, speeding down a freeway, totally out of control. This feeling of powerlessness wasn't helped by a constant litany of bad news regarding my condition, especially in relation to platelets (blood clotting agents) and T-cells. It was very difficult to maintain any sort of bright outlook, when everything that we seemed to try failed to have any prolonged effect.

I have always had a belief in God, although this was certainly put to the test. Growing up I was told that God would get me if I did something wrong. Well, God had certainly got me this time, so I believed that I must have done something wrong! I thought that I had resolved my sexuality fifteen years previously. Obviously I hadn't. It seemed logical to me at this time to assume that my punishment was for being gay. This feeling of being punished by God certainly helped to intensify my general feeling of powerlessness.

At the very outset of this period of my life I resolved to use whatever means and facilities were available to help me physically and emotionally. Warm, compassionate doctors, naturopaths and counsellors certainly helped, as did contact with Acceptance (a Gay Catholic organisation). A priest I spoke to helped me to get back in touch with God. It was wonderful. I felt able to communicate with Him again. I was able to say that I wasn't at all impressed with things and I didn't like the fact that I had been chosen to win this part of life's lottery. This mere fact of speaking to God helped to lessen that feeling of lacking control that was so overwhelming in my life.

Meanwhile the blood problem continued. My haematologist continued to offer support and treatment, and after many disappointments that problem was eventually brought under control.

As I undertook to do more things to create a healing environment for myself: diet; surgery; medication (in this case AZT); vitamin supplements; meditation; counselling and most importantly, learning to like myself, I seemed to regain control over my life.

It would be nice to finish this story by saying that everything is now fine. It would be nice to report that I am well, physically and emotionally. It would be nice to say that the future now looks bright and I am never depressed or angry or frightened. It would be nice to say that I am cured. It *would* be nice to say these things but unfortunately it wouldn't be true. I still have the AIDS virus and there are certainly still signs of things going wrong with my body.

As I see it, life now is a constant learning experience, complete with good times and bad times. It just goes on. For me the big difference is that I am finding that I love life and I am finding it a lot easier to accept my feelings, whatever they are. It probably seems strange to say so, but I am actually very grateful to the AIDS virus because it has taught me so many wonderful lessons I am sure I would otherwise never have learned.

'And they all lived happily ever after...' As a child all stories seemed to end this way. Having had some of my new-found friends die recently, I am beginning to realise that this is not what life is about. I may live to an old age or I might die soon. Perhaps that's not the real issue. The real issue, for me, is just to live life today. Yes, I plan for the future, but I try to cherish each moment that I have on this Earth.

Available Tapes

The following tapes have been produced by Petrea. Several more tapes are presently in the planning stage and will be directed towards imagery, dealing with depression and basic techniques for children. Please write to the address below if you would like to be on the mailing list, and to order tapes. As from 1989 the cost of tapes is $U.S.18 including postage and packing. Write beforehand to check on the current price of tapes if you wish. Please allow one month for delivery.

Learning to Meditate

An excellent tape for those starting out on their meditation practice. The first side of the tape explains the practical considerations necessary to ensure quality to your meditation practice. On the other side is a meditation exercise.

Learning to Visualise

The perfect complement to the tape above. A firm understanding of the principles and practice of visualisation is given. Guided imagery is used to bring the listener into a calm and healing state.

Relaxation — with Guided Imagery for the Immune System

A guided relaxation followed by a visualisation technique to assist the immune system to function at its best. This tape is used extensively in hospitals around Australia — particularly for those patients who are infected with the HIV.

Sleep Easy

No-one has ever heard the end of this tape! Designed both for the chronic insomniac and those who are having temporary difficulty in finding deep and restful sleep.

Working with Pain

The 'Rotation of Awareness' is an ancient yogic technique which is extremely valuable in calming the body and mind. It is very effective for those who are in chronic or acute pain. The second technique is an exploration into the nature of pain and is another excellent source of relief.

Increasing Self Esteem

This tape offers guidance for improving self esteem so that in learning to love yourself, you are more open to receiving love, and giving love to others, thus bringing an extra-special quality to life.

Guided Imagery Tapes — Soar Like an Eagle

A guided meditation that allows you to use your own imagination to its fullest, bringing you to experience new levels of peace and joy. An inner journey to the mountaintop and beyond.

A complete list of tapes will be sent on request. Details of seminars covering the topics discussed in this book can also be sent on request. To order tapes please send full details and cheque or money order to:

Petrea King, P.O. Box 267, CAMMERAY, NSW, 2062 AUSTRALIA

Suggested Reading

Benson, Herbert, *The Relaxation Response,* Avon, 1976, New York.
Cousins, Norman, *Anatomy of an Illness,* Bantam, 1979, New York.
Cousins, Norman, *The Healing Heart,* Avon, 1983, New York.
Gawler, Ian, *You can Conquer Cancer,* Hill of Content, 1984, Melbourne.
Gawler, Ian, *Peace of Mind,* Hill of Content, 1987, Melbourne.
Hay, Louise, *You Can Heal Your Life,* Hay House, 1987, California.
Jampolsky, Gerald, *Love is Letting Go of Fear,* Bantam, 1979, California.
Jampolsky, Gerald, *Goodbye to Guilt,* Bantam, 1987, California.
Kidman, Brenda, *A Gentle Way with Cancer,* Century, 1983, London.
Kidman, Brenda, *A Course in Miracles,* Foundations for Inner Peace, California.
Levine, Stephen, *Who Dies?,* Anchor, 1982, New York.
Moody, Raymond, *Life after Life,* Bantam, 1976, New York.
Siegel, Bernie, *Love, Medicine and Miracles,* Rider, 1986, London.
Simonton, Carl and Matthews-Simonton, Stephanie, *Getting Well Again,* Bantam, 1980, New York.

INDEX